A Treasury of
GRAND OPERA

Don Giovanni, Lohengrin,
La Traviata, Faust, Aida,
Carmen, Pagliacci

EDITED,
WITH THE STORIES, HISTORY, AND MUSIC
DESCRIBED IN DETAIL BY
HENRY W. SIMON

PIANO ARRANGEMENTS BY ALBERT SIRMAY
TRANSLATIONS BY GEORGE MEAD
ILLUSTRATIONS BY RAFAELLO BUSONI

MUSIC SUPERVISOR: WILLIAM STEINBERG

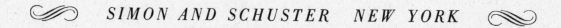 SIMON AND SCHUSTER   NEW YORK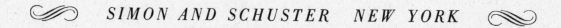

Preface

A Christmas present received over thirty years ago is indirectly responsible for this book. It was a small, badly bound collection of dreadfully simplified piano arrangements of the principal arias from several grand operas. Between the treble and bass appeared translations of the texts in the standard, unsingable "librettoese," and before each aria there were printed a few words of explanation about the plot.

Despite its palpable inadequacies, that little book inspired in my adolescent breast a love for grand opera that is today strong as ever—and as simple. I played and read it through to pieces; I saved my allowance for operatic recordings; I visited low-price opera performances as often as they were available and my resources allowed. It never occurred to me that opera might be approached either as a boring social event or as a form of musical entertainment to be regarded with suspicion because it is not "pure." Rather, through their melodic expressiveness, the tribulations of opera's several Leonoras struck me as matters for genuine concern, while Donizetti's Lucy was to me far more real than her original as chronicled by Scott. It is not, I think, surprising that words and music can be more moving than words alone, provided that the combination is approached without prejudice.

It was only after twenty years of the study and teaching of literature that I entered the musical world professionally, as a critic, and then the assignments to cover the opera were the ones I cherished most. The pathos of Violetta in the last act of La Traviata, the grim figure of Ortrud interrupting the bridal procession from Lohengrin, the three-directional pull of the final trio from Faust were as gripping as when I first encountered them. To take these music-clothed stories seriously was regarded by some of my colleagues as something quaint. Yet I believe that I had more fun than most of them at the performances; and as I have studied the aesthetics of the question, I believe that I am right—along with the millions of others who enjoy opera in a direct and simple way.

ABOUT OPERA

For it seems to me no exaggeration to say that grand opera, as developed in the eighteenth and nineteenth centuries, has given us the most enduring, the most popular, and, in their own way, the most emotionally realistic of all stage works.

Certain plays, like Lightnin', Abie's Irish Rose, Tobacco Road, *and* Life with Father *have had much longer continuous runs than any one grand opera has had, while many movies are seen by a larger number of people in one or two seasons. But who would want to sit through a performance of* Lightnin' *twenty years after its hey-day, and who can thrill to a movie "epic" like* Ben Hur *once its techniques look old-fashioned?*

A half dozen plays of Shakespeare's (but only of Shakespeare's) have endured with sufficient vigor to be often revived. But where is the dramatic stock company that, for over thirty years, can travel up and down the land giving the same dozen shows over and over again week after week to huge audiences? That is the record of the San Carlo Opera Company in the United States, while the Carl Rosa Opera Company has been doing it twice as long in England. The sixty-year history of the Metropolitan Opera has been made possible by the undiminished appeal of the same dozen or fifteen operas, and so has the history of the Covent Garden seasons in England and of dozens of opera houses on the European continent. The Fausts *and the* Aïdas *have had thousands of performances each and millions of listeners. They have been loved by all sorts and conditions of men and women, sung by all sorts and conditions of casts. To survive so many years and such fre-*

quent mishandling, there must be some basic appeal, something very real that these works have to offer.

This something real lies, I believe, in the very nature of grand opera itself, and is a form of realism practically impossible to achieve in spoken drama. Spoken drama, because it deals in dialogue and action only, must focus on those comparatively few moments in our lives when something important is happening, usually in the presence of others. Such moments, however dramatic they may be, are likely to be less intimately real—even less intense—than the much larger share of our emotional lives—the times when we feel strongly about something or other but can do nothing active about it. It is the projection of emotion at such times, through words and music both, that makes certain passages of opera so real as to be almost unbearable.

Take, for example, the popular "Ridi, Pagliaccio" aria. Suppose that in a spoken play a simple and violently emotional Italian actor discovers that his adored and butterflyish wife is planning to elope with an unknown young man. In a little while, the player knows, he must go on the stage to act out a very similar situation with his own wife as leading lady. The play-within-the-play situation is common enough on the stage. But what could a modern realistic playwright do with such a situation? He could either rely on the actor to get across the conflict within himself through a gesture or two, or he could have him discuss it with a friend. Either device would give a distorted picture of what might be expected to happen in real life. For the most important, most moving, part of this man's experience would be the time he has to spend by himself before the evening's performance. Grand opera can, and does, paint this part of his experience as no other art can. It builds up to such scenes, just as spoken drama is likely to build up to scenes of action. Opera also has scenes of action quite as dramatic as these plays, but they fade into comparative insignificance beside the intense reality of the scenes of emotional climax. Few opera-goers remember the music played when Canio finally stabs Nedda in Pagliacci, when Radames surrenders his sword in Aïda, when Lohengrin slays Telramund in Lohengrin. In terms of spoken drama, these are important climaxes; but the great moments of grand opera come rather in the more realistic, less stagey parts—when Radames lyrically longs to become a vic-

torious general so that he may elevate his beloved to a throne ("Celeste Aïda"), when Violetta attempts to persuade herself that it is too late to hang on to hopes of seeing Alfredo again ("Addio del passato"), or when Faust, standing alone in Marguerite's garden, first senses the natural beauty that frames her innocence ("Salut! demeure").

But the aria is only one element of grand opera in which emotional realism is more striking than it is in the spoken drama. When there are two or more characters on the stage, each with his own emotions to project, the superiority of opera over the spoken drama is even greater. In a play, one character expresses his emotions and then another. In life, these emotions are felt simultaneously, and so they are expressed in opera. It is possible in duets, trios, and such great concerted numbers as appear in Aïda, La Traviata, Don Giovanni and Lohengrin, to picture many conflicting emotions at the same time, and to make their combined impact produce an overwhelming experience for the listener utterly impossible to produce through any other art.

These, I think, are the real reasons why many thousands go to hear La Traviata every year while the Dumas play from which it stems is seldom revived; why even more thousands hear Bizet's Carmen while Mérimée's novelette remains an occasional exercise in college French; why practically only Germans ever see a performance of Goethe's Faust and all the world keeps buying seats to hear Gounod's. The semi-educated snob is likely to regard grand opera as more or less good music haphazardly married to stories (sometimes preposterous) and stage action (often ridiculous). But the snob is wrong about this, as he always is about everything, while the ordinary people who buy tickets at the box-office are right, as Verdi insisted they must be. Gluck and Wagner both said it in written words, and every lover of opera knows it instinctively: an operatic story is not a vehicle for good music; rather, music is a help in the poignant expression of real feelings in a story that the composer takes with utter seriousness.

For Americans this is a difficult idea to accept. It is our custom to give operas in the original language instead of in the language of the audience, as is done in every continental European country. Our audiences are likely to understand only the general drift of a story and to be further put off from sympathizing with the emotions expressed by the middle European or Italian traditions of mounting and directing the works. Yet, unless one knows the intimate details of the stories and has some sympathy with them, grand opera becomes a series of tunes punctuated by boredom.

For this reason, I have included in this book only operas with stage-worthy stories. I have summarized the literary and stage history of each work and tried to indicate the reasons for its great success. Then I have described in detail exactly what happens on the stage both dramatically and musically, keeping in mind the fact that for millions radio still affords the only means for hearing complete operas. I hope that it may be possible to sit by the radio during an opera broadcast and follow the action and music in detail with a copy of this book in your lap. I also hope that individuals, as well as groups in the good old custom of standing around the piano and singing, will enjoy going over the most memorable pages of music.

ABOUT MY COLLABORATORS' WORK

There are forty to fifty pages from the score of each opera given here in arrangements that can be played with voices or without, as the melody is always kept in the piano part. Dr. Albert Sirmay, one of the most widely experienced music editors in America today, and I had endless discussions about these arrangements. We had to plan on what numbers to include in the space available, when to transpose so that the untrained voice might be able to cope with the music, how to get as much musical value as possible into the arrangements without making them unplayable. Then, after all the arrangements had been worked out initially, I also consulted with William Steinberg, one of the most distinguished operatic conductors in the world and a brilliant concert pianist. Some of the arrangements we barely touched, a few Mr. Steinberg completely rewrote.

It became my task, as editor of the book, to decide which of these experts to use in the few cases where there was sharp disagreement. For example, Dr. Sirmay had made a very simple arrangement of Don Giovanni's Serenade, sacrificing the mandolin obbligato in the interests of ease of playing. Mr. Steinberg (just for the fun of it, he said) made a brilliant piano transcription much too difficult for most amateurs but ingeniously retaining the several rhythmical patterns Mozart employed simultaneously. I solved this particular dilemma by retaining the brilliant transcription but using it only for the second stanza of the Serenade. The only other really difficult pages in the book occur in the middle section of "Salut! demeure" from Faust, where Mr. Steinberg managed to weave in the beautiful violin obbligato almost exactly as Gounod wrote it. Mr. Steinberg's intimate and exact knowledge of the orchestral scores, as a matter of fact, was of service on practically every page in a little touch here and a little touch there, but it is Dr. Sirmay's wide experience as a piano arranger that has formed the basis of a majority of the arrangements. These two gifted gentlemen worked on the arrangements in different towns and never met. I had to make all the final decisions when they were to be made; and the reader therefore must hold me responsible for any errors of judgment he may discern.

Lack of space has made necessary some arbitrary cuts. To give, for example, the entire "Ritorna vincitor" from Aïda would have meant omitting at least one other number from that opera. We have, therefore, given only the major portion of the second and more melodious part of that aria and used a title taken from the first line of that part (There Is No Other). But most of the numbers are complete, and all of them make perfectly good musical sense as they stand.*

Excepting in the brief musical quotations in my descriptions of the operas, the English translations have been specially made for this book by George Mead. These translations strike me as a triumph of ingenuity and good taste. Mr. Mead, who is both a singer and a linguist, has written lyrics that one can sing or read aloud without feeling sorry for the King's English: every line is clear, simple, idiomatic, singable. Even the originals do not always exhibit these merits in their own languages. Anyone who doubts the great artfulness shown here need only examine the average standard opera libretto to see how this job is usually done.

Rafaello Busoni's illustrations, decorative as they are, represent no mere effort to make the book prettier. Mr. Busoni has had extensive experience as a stage

* Familiar tempo markings, such as *adagio, andante,* and *allegro,* have been retained. Less familiar Italian directions about expression, such as *affretando, perendosi,* etc., I have translated or paraphrased. Most of the ties in the vocal musical lines have been eliminated in the interests of clarity and consistency.

designer, and his illustrations are based on a re-study of the operas and a sound conception of what the characters, costumes and sets might look like in a finely imaginative production. They capture the romantic spirit of these operas and make vivid, as no words could, what you might be seeing on the stage if only productions were as good as they ought to be.

One more paragraph of appreciation must be devoted to Andor Braun, artist and musician, who designed this book, and to Miss Kay Margolis, whose efficiency and good nature were not jarred even fractionally by the tortuous process of seeing it through the press.

To my collaborators, then, my deepest respect and sincerest thanks—especially for the patience, taste and high intelligence with which they have worked in solving the many problems this project has presented.

H. W. S.

CONTENTS

Don Giovanni

Lohengrin

La Traviata

Faust

Aïda

Carmen

Pagliacci

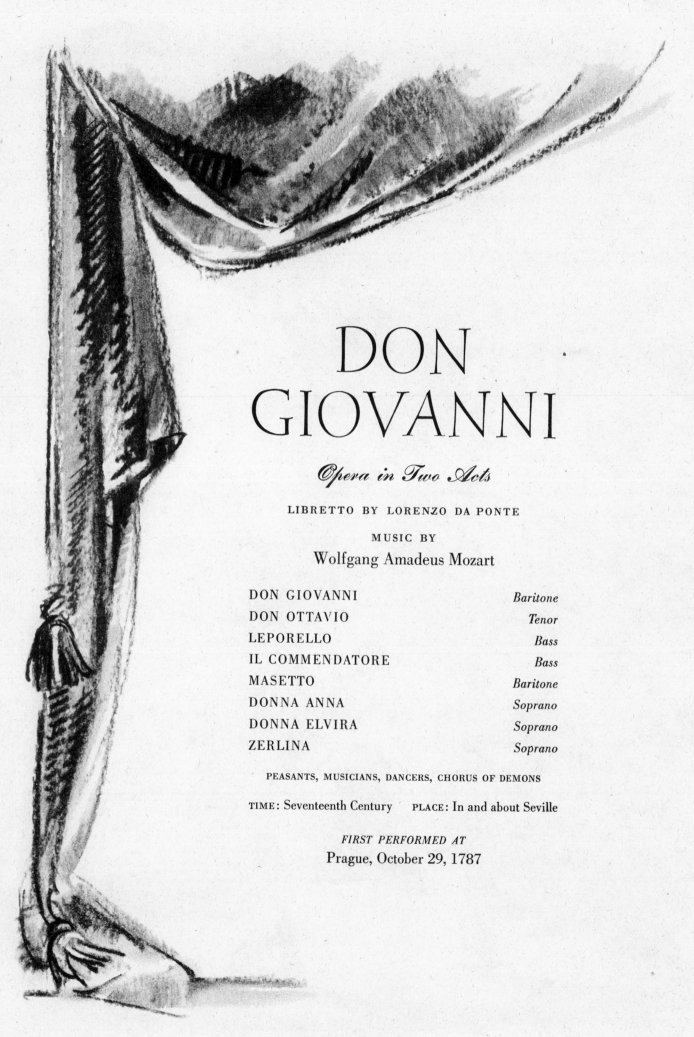

DON GIOVANNI

Opera in Two Acts

LIBRETTO BY LORENZO DA PONTE

MUSIC BY

Wolfgang Amadeus Mozart

DON GIOVANNI	*Baritone*
DON OTTAVIO	*Tenor*
LEPORELLO	*Bass*
IL COMMENDATORE	*Bass*
MASETTO	*Baritone*
DONNA ANNA	*Soprano*
DONNA ELVIRA	*Soprano*
ZERLINA	*Soprano*

PEASANTS, MUSICIANS, DANCERS, CHORUS OF DEMONS

TIME: Seventeenth Century   PLACE: In and about Seville

FIRST PERFORMED AT
Prague, October 29, 1787

Don Giovanni

WOLFGANG AMADEUS MOZART

A FEW years ago when, in the course of a review, I referred to *Don Giovanni* as a comedy, a musical friend wrote to ask whether I did not realize it was really a tragedy.

That is a question which has bothered critics for well over a hundred years—ever since, in fact, E. T. A. Hoffmann (the man about whom *The Tales of Hoffmann* was written) started to find in the work sad and solemn truths which neither composer nor librettist had, apparently, ever thought of. Even today many people—like my friend—feel uncomfortable when this divine work is referred to the way its creators referred to it. Da Ponte, the author, called it a *dramma giocoso* (a jolly play) on the title page of the first libretto; Mozart, the composer, listed it as an *opera buffa* (light opera) in a catalogue of his works.

What has bothered these critics is, first of all, that there is one scene—the one in which the statue of the Commandant accepts Don Giovanni's dinner invitation—that is too terrifying to find a legitimate place in a light opera. In addition, there are some arias and concerted numbers—even some passages of recitative—that are so sublime, so inspiredly beautiful, that it seems an insult to the work to classify it as Da Ponte and Mozart did. The emotions of the beginning of the Overture, of the aria *"Non mi dir,"* of the trio *"Protegga il giusto cielo"* are serious emotions, and no tragic opera has ever set them forth more seriously than has *Don Giovanni*.

Yet it is true that many light operas have passages that deal seriously with love, fear, and prayer; and I dare say that if Sir Arthur Sullivan or Victor Herbert or Jerome Kern had had the genius, each would have been glad to compose music as great as Mozart's, and in the same vein. The fact is that the predominant mood of *Don Giovanni* is light, that its creators thought of it as predominantly light, and that music is no less beautiful because it is composed for a light opera instead of a tragic one. I think it is safe to say that, with the possible exception of Mozart's *Marriage of Figaro*, his *Don Giovanni* is the greatest light opera ever written.

Everything about the history of its composition confirms the idea that Mozart intended it as a light opera. In Prague, the hit of the season of 1786-87 had been *Figaro*. Mozart, who was there in January of that season, wrote to a friend: "Nothing is talked of here but *Figaro*; no opera is cared for but *Figaro*; always *Figaro*——" Everyone was whistling the tunes, everyone danced to them. *"Non più andrai"* was on the hit parade. So delighted was the manager of the Italian Opera, whose season had been saved from financial disaster by the success of this one opera, that he immediately accepted Mozart's suggestion for another work especially written for Prague. The fee was the customary hundred ducats,* and Mozart chose the same librettist he had used for *Figaro*, Lorenzo da Ponte.

I wish there were space here for a fuller biography of this Da Ponte. Born a Venetian Jew, he had been trained for the priesthood, had taught literature in the seminary at Treviso, had been forced to flee various towns and jobs on account of his unorthodox opinions and ways with women, and was now official "Poet to the Italian Theaters" at Vienna. Later on he was to become a bookseller and fugitive from justice in London, a greengrocer in New Jersey, a wine merchant and real-estate man in Pennsylvania, a pamphleteer and impresario in New York, and Columbia University's first official professor of Italian. At all times, to judge from his spicy and self-adulatory *Memoirs*, he was in love with life, literature, laughter, and love. He was an adventurer of the type of Cellini and Casanova, and he was acquainted with the latter. There is even

---

*A hundred ducats would have been the equivalent of about $225 in the American silver dollars of Mozart's day. It sounds like little enough for what many musicians have considered the greatest opera ever composed. In terms of what the money could buy in Austria, however, Bondini, the manager, can scarcely be considered niggardly. For the best house he ever lived in, complete with billiard room, Mozart paid a rental of only ninety-two ducats a year; the yearly salary he earned as official composer to Emperor Joseph II was 164 ducats; the yearly salary earned by his housemaid was two ducats a year and keep. The fourth performance of the opera was a benefit for the composer, in addition to the hundred ducats—and Bondini, after all, could not be sure, before he had seen a note of it, that *Don Giovanni* would be a success. For *Figaro*, Mozart had received considerably less.

pretty good circumstantial evidence that Casanova made some specific suggestions about the libretto for *Don Giovanni*.

It would be hard to imagine a man better suited spiritually to be the author of *Don Giovanni* than the Abbé da Ponte, as he styled himself. At the same time that he was writing it, he was working on two other librettos; and when the Emperor Joseph II objected that perhaps he was doing too much, he replied that it was quite simple. He would work on *Tarare* for Salieri in the morning, for Martini on *L'Arbore di Diana* in the afternoon, and for Mozart on *Don Giovanni* at night. And, he adds in his *Memoirs*, he finished all but *Tarare* in sixty-three days with the help of a box of snuff, a good supply of wine, and the amatory dalliance of his landlady's pretty daughter.

Perhaps *Don Giovanni* was the easiest of the three to complete, for a good deal of it was closely fashioned after the libretto of *Il Convitato di Pietra (The Stone Guest)*, a popular opera of the time by Giuseppe Gazzaniga and Giovanni Bertati. Some passages of Mozart's music also appear to be based on this opera; and if anyone still doubts that the inspiration for *Don Giovanni* was light, he would do well to consult Bertati's libretto and note its low-comedy tone.

There were other models of greater or less seriousness to which Mozart and Da Ponte might have turned, for the tale is an old one. No one knows just how old, for the similar tales said to have been current in monasteries of the Middle Ages are no longer extant, and no one knows whether Don Juan Tenorio of Seville was a real man or a legend. Pre-Da Ponte dramatic treatments include the Spanish play by Tirso de Molina (or Gabriel Tellez), which dates from 1630, Molière's comedy *Don Juan, ou le Festin de Pierre* (1665), and Thomas Shadwell's serious treatment, *The Libertine Destroyed*. There was also an anonymous and very popular low-comedy version acted by strolling players in Italy which Da Ponte might well have known. As for musical ideas, Mozart might have turned to Gluck, who had composed a ballet on the subject, to Le Tellier, who had composed a light French opera, and also, of course, to Gazzaniga.

The conditions under which the composing was completed would certainly lead one to suspect that Mozart had no world-shaking philosophical thoughts on his mind. Much of the score was probably composed in Vienna between June 24 and August 10, 1787, when, according to Mozart's own catalogue, no other composi-

tion was completed. In September he went back to Prague with his wife Constanze and settled down to finish the work in the Villa Bertramka.

This villa belonged to a coloratura soprano named Josefa Duschek, and Josefa must have been one of those original Bohemians whose temperament and way of life have made us give the word "Bohemian" to certain kinds of artist the world over. She was gay, gifted, open-hearted, and kept open house for the musicians, actors, and poets of Prague. The house itself she was able to buy out of the money she had saved as an opera singer and (to judge from the low salaries paid most opera singers in those days) as the mistress of the wealthy Count Cristian Clam. When Josefa had parted with both the Count and her stage career, she married her old music teacher, Franz Xavier Duschek, and the two lived a merry life in the suburbs of the Bohemian capital. In the grounds of their villa there still is (or at least was before the war) the garden house where Mozart finished composing *Don Giovanni*.

This villa, too, was the setting of one of the best-known Mozart legends. The day before the *première* of October 29, 1787—so the story runs—the Overture had not yet been written down. Mozart, perhaps, had been spending too much time between rehearsals playing games and carousing with his genial hosts. Late at night he started with a supply of punch on the table and his wife beside him to keep him awake by telling him stories. Part way through he fell asleep for several hours but awoke in time to have the music in the hands of the copyists by 7 A.M. Actually, the Overture bears the date October 28 in Mozart's own hand, and it may be that he really had it ready in time for the dress rehearsal. Whatever the truth, it remains a good story, and Mozart is said to have congratulated the little orchestra that night on doing a good job of sight reading.

Another story connected with the first performance concerns Caterina Bondini, the impresario's wife, who had the role of Zerlina. Mozart was dissatisfied at the rehearsals with the scream she gave when, in the last scene of the first act, the Don is supposed to be making improper advances to her. Mozart himself thereupon undertook to make the improper advances by slipping behind her and administering a sharp pinch which elicited a convincing shriek.

In Prague, the opera was a great success from the first. In Vienna, where it was mounted the following year with certain additions, it gained favor much more slowly. London first heard it in April, 1817; New York on May 23, 1826. The American *première* was given at the instigation of Da Ponte, with Manuel García, a tenor and the impresario of the troupe, singing the baritone title role, García's wife Donna Elvira, his son Leporello, and his daughter Zerlina. This daughter, Maria, later developed into one of the most skillful and romantically beloved opera singers of the day under her married name of Malibran.

The opera was a fair success at the time, but it became a real hit only later, when it was given in English. In the 1830's and 40's no one (quite sensibly) thought of giving it in New York in any language other than the one the audience could understand, and Malibran often sang the part in English too. Since then our opera companies, through either laziness or misguided theories of aesthetics, have given it in Italian.

Today *Don Giovanni* is by no means the most popular opera in the general repertoire. Almost certainly it has received fewer American performances than any other opera discussed in this book. One reason is that it requires not only a pair of first-class singing actors for the roles of the Don and Leporello, but also three sopranos who can sing extraordinarily difficult music with both skill and taste. The last seems to be a rare commodity.

Nevertheless, outside of Mozart's *Marriage of Figaro*, it is the oldest opera given regularly in practically every country of the Western world. For over a century and a half it has been part of the staple repertoire. Occasionally the Metropolitan and other great opera houses will mount an even older opera, like one of Gluck's or Pergolesi's, but Mozart's great works maintain enough popular appeal, year after year, to be considered as timeless as any opera ever composed.

As for the regard of great musicians, I shall close this prefatory note by quoting the words of a few other famous opera composers:

"He is the greatest—the master of them all—the only composer who had as much skill as he had genius and as much genius as he had skill." *(Rossini, upon inspecting the autograph of* Don Giovanni.*)*

"The score of *Don Giovanni* has exercised the influence of a revelation upon the whole of my life; it has been and remains for me a kind of incarnation of dramatic and musical impeccability. I regard it as a work without blemish, of uninterrupted perfection." *(Gounod, in the preface to an analysis of the score published to commemorate the hundredth anniversary of its first performance.)*

"Is it possible to find anything more perfect than every piece in *Don Giovanni?* . . . Where else has music won so infinitely rich an individuality, been able to characterize so surely, so definitely, and in such exuberant plenitude as here?" *(Wagner, in* Opera and Drama.*)*

Overture

MOST Mozart opera overtures are simply pieces that set the mood for what is to follow. The first thirty bars of the Overture to *Don Giovanni* depart from this custom. Rhythmically and melodically, they are closely based on the opera's most dramatically impressive scene. This occurs at the end of the work, when the ghost of the Commandant of Seville interrupts the Don's dinner to accept the invitation given earlier. The Commandant enters on a thunderclap and addresses Don Giovanni in sepulchral tones to music that is almost identical with the Overture's opening eight bars:

The Don, frightened for the first time in the opera, tries to regain his *savoir-faire* to the slowly syncopated measures that follow:

No. 1
Andante

No. 2
Andante

But finally the Commandant summons Don Giovanni to hell to the accompaniment of a series of scales that look quite simple in the score but can be really terrifying when performed with a large crescendo followed by a sudden piano:

No. 3
Andante

These scales, with their peculiarly dramatic effect, were an afterthought of Mozart's, according to his biographer Otto Jahn, for they appear in the autograph score in the last act squeezed in after the rest of the scene was completed. In the original of the Overture, however, they appear just as large as all the other passages. As the Overture was composed last of all, Jahn concludes that he must have thought of the effect when the opera was virtually completed.

Once this introduction to the Introduction is over, the music runs along in the most chattery, busy fashion, quite in keeping with the light comedy that is the main business of the evening. These are its two principal themes:

No. 4
Molto allegro

and

No. 5
Molto allegro

Various commentators have tried to find philosophical significance in these themes too, but it scarcely seems to be necessary. After that solemn, opening andante, this Overture remains as bubbly and full of irrepressible good humor as the Overture to *Nozze di Figaro* itself. Nothing could be happier than that.

The original version of the Overture (as opposed to the one usually heard in concert) has no formal ending but goes at once into the lumbering introduction to Leporello's opening words:

No. 6
Molto allegro

Act One, Scene 1

AT night, in a handsome garden before a handsome house, lurks Leporello, the humorously surly, heartless, weak-charactered servant and confidant of Don Giovanni. Inside, as he tells us, the Don is at his love-making, while he himself must stand guard. Nobody would like his job. The pay is poor, so is the food provided, and the duties keep you up day and night. Besides, Leporello himself would like to play the gentleman; and so he threatens to leave this bootless service. It is one of his favorite threats. But before he is through singing, he thinks he hears the Don coming out of the house and—quite characteristically— hides behind a bush so that he may at once be safe and also do a bit of eavesdropping.

It is the Don, all right, whom Leporello has heard, and he is engaged in equally characteristic business. He is trying to get away from Donna Anna, after a virtuoso attempt to seduce her without disclosing his identity. At the moment she is hanging on to him, trying to find out who he is while he is attempting three things at once—to hide his face in his cloak, to persuade Donna Anna to remain quiet, and to make his getaway. But in this particular escapade, the virtuoso seducer has mis-

judged his prey, for Donna Anna, though she fails to identify him, calls for help and swears to pursue him "with desperate fury." All of which, of course, gives Mozart an excellent opportunity for a trio in which the Don and the Donna express their conflicting emotions simultaneously while Leporello, on the other side of the stage, comments sardonically on his libertine master.

The Don manages to free himself from Donna Anna's furious grasp only when she hears her father, the Commandant of Seville, storming out of the house. Dressed in a night robe, he carries a drawn sword in one hand and a lamp in the other. While Donna Anna rushes into the house for help, the Commandant challenges the Don, who contemptuously warns him that he had better not try to fight. The old gentleman, however, persists, sarcastically suggesting that the Don is trying to run away. According to the Don's ideas about honor, there remains nothing to do but have it out. Efficiently, he first knocks the lamp out of the old gentleman's hand so that he will not be recognized, and then proceeds to kill him in a pathetically brief duel.

Meantime, Leporello, hiding in the bushes, wishes he could get away somehow, and emerges only when the fight is over. The moon slowly rises during the hasty whispers that follow.

"Who's dead?" asks Leporello. "You or the old gent?" And when he finds out, he congratulates his master ironically: "Bravo! a couple of nice jobs—to attack the daughter and murder the father."

"He insisted on it," says the Don in self-defense.

"But Donna Anna. Did she also insist?"

As usual, when he is put in the wrong by Leporello, the Don ends the argument by threatening to beat him, and the two run off—just in time. For Donna Anna has managed to summon help—some servants, who come in with torches, and her fiancé, Don Ottavio. This Don, intended as a noble, tragic character in the classic conventions, strikes modern audiences as one of the most futile lovers in opera; for actually, with the best of intentions, he never accomplishes anything and seldom rises to an occasion with any true romantic feeling. The music Mozart has composed for him, however, has all the beauty and compassion we feel lacking in his actions.

Seeing the body of her father, Donna Anna flings herself on the corpse and bursts into lamentation. Don Ottavio tries to raise her, but overcome by her grief, she repulses him. The unhappy young man can think of nothing better to do than send for smelling salts and wring his hands over her; and then, while the servants carry out the body, she turns furiously upon him almost as though he had been responsible for the tragedy. Little by little, he manages to calm her; and he sings two beautiful phrases, the first of which bears a close resemblance to the comforting music of the Blessed Spirits in Gluck's *Orfeo*:

No. 7
Allegro

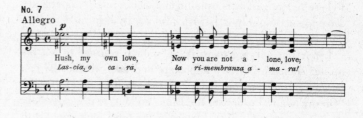

Hush, my own love, Now you are not a - lone, love;
Las-cia o ca - ra, la ri-membranza a - ma - ra!

You have hus-band and fa - ther in me.
hai spo - so e pa - dre in me.

Solemnly she makes him swear to avenge her dead father, and the scene ends with a duet in which they both take this oath.

Act One, Scene 2

LIKE many other opera librettos, *Don Giovanni* is not very specific about the amount of time supposed to elapse between scenes. The second scene, however, may, as well as not, take place a couple of hours or less after the first. It is early in the morning on a square just outside of Seville, and Don Giovanni is carrying on one of his rapid-fire recitatives with Leporello. (These recitatives, as is usual in eighteenth-century opera, are accompanied only by a harpsichord or, in most modern productions, a piano.)

Leporello is trying to work up enough courage to tell his master something pretty important and asks whether he can be guaranteed freedom from punishment if he speaks freely. "On my honor," promises the Don, "so long as it is not about the Commandant." Still, Leporello hesitates long enough to make sure that there is no one around, and then he utters this profound thought:

"Dear Sir Patron," he says, "the life you are leading"—and he leans over to shout in Sir Patron's ear—"is that of a bum!"

Don Giovanni is—as usual—about to strike Leporello; but, when Leporello promises to shut up, he becomes good-natured again and asks whether his servant knows why they have come to this place. Leporello doesn't have to think very hard to answer that one. "Since it's just about dawn," he says, "what is more likely than some new conquest? I'll have to know her name, though, so that I can put her down in the list."

He has guessed right, of course. The Don says he is in love with a beautiful lady he has seen and spoken to, and he is loved in turn by her. Tonight they are to meet at the casino. Suddenly he stops. "Sh!" he shushes. "It seems to me I sense the odor of femininity."

"What a nose!" murmurs Leporello.

"And out here in the open air, I should say she's beautiful."

"And what an eye!"

And they retire to the back of the stage, while Donna Elvira enters in a traveling dress and proceeds to pour out her heart in an aria ("*Ah, chi mi dice mai*") full of beautiful Mozartean melodic phrases and broad skips of an octave and more. Elvira, we learn, is searching everywhere for the lover who has seduced her with protestations of love and called her his wife. Her typically feminine reason for wanting to find the man again is simply that she may now spurn him. For the difference in the characters of Donna Anna and Donna Elvira (not always made clear by the sketchy acting that sopranos give the two roles) lies in Anna's inflexible and practical determination to have bloody vengeance on the Don and Donna Elvira's soft, sentimental determination to ease her own hurt feelings. She is the more futile character of the two, but also the more lovable.

While Donna Elvira sings this aria, Leporello, at the back of the stage, tries to get a look at her (a bit of pantomime that can almost ruin the lovely music), and the Don remarks, with a sort of sardonic pity, that grief becomes this lady very well indeed.

At the close of the number the Don steps politely forward and offers his help. Only then does he discover that he himself is the man of whom she has been complaining, since she is a lady whom he had tired of and abandoned after a three-day elopement to Burgos.* Immediately she begins to upbraid him—as she had promised herself she would—while he starts to make excuses and calls on Leporello to witness the validity

---

*The librettist is vague about what actually happened beween Donna Elvira and Don Giovanni. Here she says that he declared her his wife and later on she refers to him several times as her husband. Critics seem to assume that this is just the unfortunate lady's delusion, but it may well be that Mozart and Da Ponte thought of the two being legally, if clandestinely, married. The possibility is strengthened by the fact that in Molière's play on the subject (which, of course, antedates the opera) the Don and the Donna were actually married. If they were also married in the opera, Don Giovanni becomes even more of a villain and Donna Elvira less fatuous.

of the reasons for his hasty departure from Burgos. She, of course, refuses to believe him; and while she has her back turned in contempt, the Don tells Leporello to "tell her all" and manages to slip away before she can catch him again.

Leporello's way of telling Elvira all, and thereby bringing her consolation, is one of the oddest in the world. "Look," he says, "you haven't been the first he has deserted and you won't be the last." And he takes out a book from which a long stretch of paper coils across the stage as he reads her the list of the Don's conquests. This is the "*Madamina*" patter song. In Italy, he sings, there were 640, in Germany 231, a hundred in France, ninety-one in Turkey, but in Spain—here comes the grand climax—1003! (The total, which Leporello does not bother to tot up, is 2065.) Furthermore, the list includes women of every rank, shape, and complexion—coun-tesses, servant girls, city ladies, baronesses, marchionesses, princesses. The technique used by the Don, continues Leporello, is to praise blondes for their gentleness and sweetness, brunettes for their constancy. In the winter he likes them a bit on the plump side, in the summer rather thinner. He likes both great, majestic creatures and little minxes, and he has a weakness for getting some of the older ladies down on his list too. However, the predominating passion is for young ones. And, he concludes with the ultimate touch of tactfulness, Donna Elvira herself knows pretty well how successful the Don is! With which Leporello also makes a hasty exit.

Temporarily, at least, Donna Elvira is roused to a more aggressive frame of mind. As the curtain goes down, she says that she now despises the Don and that she will be truly revenged on him.

Act One, Scene 3

THE next scene—apparently still the same day—takes place in a pretty, rural spot near Don Giovanni's castle on the outskirts of Seville. Villagers are singing and dancing, celebrating the engagement of a pretty girl named Zerlina to her village swain, Masetto, who is usually acted like a much stupider young fellow than he seems to be after one has read the libretto. The sweet little chorus the villagers sing ends as the two young lovers are surrounded by a ring of their friends.

The Don and Leporello, reunited after their successive escapes from Donna Elvira, come upon this rustic scene, and the Don almost at once picks out the just-engaged Zerlina for his next attempt at amorous conquest. With the most gallant condescension, he congratulates the happy young couple and invites the entire company to come into his castle, where Leporello is to show them his gardens, his rooms, his pictures. His plan, of course, is to send the others upstairs and keep Zerlina in the garden with him. He pokes Leporello in the ribs as he gives him instructions to take particular care of Masetto. That young man is at once suspicious and protests that he cannot leave Zerlina. Nor is he in the least reassured when Leporello, the Don, and Zerlina herself all point out that she is in the hands of a nobleman. Even when the Don warns him by tapping the hilt of his sword, Masetto continues to protest bitterly. "Always trust a gentleman," he ironically repeats over and over again. His resentment of the eighteenth-century aristocrat's attitude toward the sanctity of a lower-class marriage is quite as great as Figaro's in *The Marriage of Figaro*. Unfortunately, his fiancée is more dangerously flirtatious than Figaro's, and all that Masetto can do for the moment is to continue to protest as Leporello hustles him off.

With Masetto out of the way, the Don goes to work at once. It is obvious, he says, that nature never meant Zerlina to be married to such a low fellow as that Masetto. She was meant to marry a noble. Zerlina points out that she has promised to marry Masetto the next day—a promise that is worth, says the Don, exactly zero. Zerlina is still resistant (in a very artful way, of course) and suggests that the reputation of noblemen, when it comes to ladies, is not noted for honesty and sincerity. "A plebeian slander," says the Don, and he invites Zerlina to his castle, where, he says, he will marry her at once.

The duet that follows is so charming that it had to be sung over three times at the opera's *première*. Thereafter encores were forbidden. The Don, without too much difficulty, persuades Zerlina that his intentions are honorable, and she agrees to give them a try (see p. 18). Toward the close of the duet, Donna Elvira comes on the scene and sees what is going on. Just as the couple are about to go to the castle, Elvira dramatically interrupts and denounces the Don and his intentions, of which, as she points out, she has had firsthand experience. He tries to whisper to Elvira that this is only a pastime, and to Zerlina that Elvira is only a poor wretch suffering from jealousy. A short, dramatic—almost melodramatic—aria by Elvira, however, prevents his getting away with it this time, and Zerlina allows herself to be saved for the moment. With both women off the stage, the Don remarks that the Devil himself seems to be getting in the way of everything he's doing today.

And speaking of the Devil, in come Donna Anna and Don Ottavio, still discussing the revenge they have sworn on her father's murderer (whose identity they still, of course, do not know). Ironically, they appeal to Don Giovanni himself for help, which he is delighted to promise them. But now Elvira comes back on the scene and urges them not to trust in the Don. A remarkable quartet follows in which Donna Anna and Don Ottavio are impressed by Donna Elvira's protests. They are particularly impressed by her being a member of the nobility. Meanwhile, Elvira continues her denunciations while Don Giovanni tries alternately to persuade her to behave in a less spectacular fashion and to assure the other two that the lady is slightly out of her mind. Finally he manages to lead

her away. The poor thing, is his parting comment to the others, needs someone to keep her from suicide.*

Suddenly the truth dawns on Donna Anna. In agitated accents she describes to Don Ottavio the invasion of her bedroom by an unknown man whom she at first took for Ottavio himself. A violent struggle ended (to Ottavio's evident relief) in her frightening the intruder away; but her father followed him and was murdered. Now, she says, she has recognized the man: he was Don Giovanni. Then, in an aria of great strength and nobility, she calls upon Don Ottavio once more to swear vengeance and leaves the stage.

The rather one-track mind of Don Ottavio can scarcely believe that a nobleman could behave so badly; but he swears, nevertheless, to help Donna Anna and sings the serene aria "*Dalla sua pace*," a beautiful melody that Mozart added after the initial performance in order to make the leading tenor look a little less like a superficial ornament (see p. 24).

Leporello now comes back, again resolving to leave the service of his master; but as soon as Don Giovanni appears, he reports that though matters couldn't have been going much worse with the peasants, he has handled them rather ingeniously. The Don congratulates him enthusiastically. It seems that Leporello had considerable difficulty with the jealous Masetto; but he got them all to eating and drinking, when who should come in but—as Don Giovanni guesses—Zerlina; and who should be with her but (the Don guesses correctly again) Elvira. Elvira was still at the business of cursing out the Don, but somehow Leporello managed to get her out of the house and lock the door on her.

Don Giovanni is so much delighted with this report of progress that he bursts into the light, mercurial patter song sometimes called the "Champagne" Aria (see p. 29). In it he instructs Leporello to invite all the prettiest girls he can find to his party for drinking, dancing, and nonsense unconfined. By morning, he grandiosely deludes himself, he shall have added ten more names to his list of feminine conquests.

Act One, Scene 4

THE next change of scene brings us, that evening, to the garden outside of Don Giovanni's castle, with a wing of the castle itself and its balcony visible on one side. Zerlina and Masetto are there, among the rosebushes, and they are still quarreling about the Don's outrageous prenuptial attentions to another's bride. Zerlina is all contrition and pleads that she really isn't to blame. If she was misled for a moment, she didn't *really* succumb to the nobleman. Won't Masetto believe her? He may kill her if it isn't so—and she sings the aria "*Batti, batti*," which is so tender a compound of innocence and flirtatiousness that a much more adamant swain than Masetto would be moved by it (see p. 35).

Masetto has scarcely been won over when Zerlina hears the Don giving directions for the reception of his guests, and she has a sinking feeling that maybe—just maybe—she had better

hide herself. But it is Masetto who hides, deliberately leaving the reluctant Zerlina in the dangerous Don's path and retiring to an arbor to watch. The villain enters still pursuing her, though giving directions to four servants at the same time. Zerlina tries to hide from him, but he catches her by the hand and starts pressing his suit once more. The technique this time is to draw Zerlina with him into the privacy of the arbor, where, of course, he bumps right into Masetto. Nonplused for only a moment, he tells the young man that his poor little girl has been pining away for him. Masetto is hardly convinced, but the Don, gallantly and diplomatically taking an arm of

---

*Presumably as an exercise in dramatic vocal composition in preparation for *Fidelio*. Beethoven copied out the vocal lines of this quartet. Beethoven's holograph is now owned by Walter Slezak, the actor, son of Leo Slezak, the tenor.

each of the lovers, escorts them into the castle as he invites them to his party, and they accept in a gay little trio.

Scarcely have they left when three figures in masks come on the darkening scene. They are the Donnas Elvira and Anna with Don Ottavio. Elvira and Ottavio sing of the rather indefinite revenge they hope to get on Giovanni, and Anna sings of her fears for the other two. Inside, the famous Minuet is quietly played (see p. 43) as Leporello and Don Giovanni appear on the balcony and notice the maskers. The Don instructs his servant to invite these strangers to the party; and while the music of the Minuet continues, the invitation is delivered from the balcony and courteously accepted by Don Ottavio.

Then, just before entering the castle, the three masked figures come to the footlights to sing a soft prayer that they may achieve a just revenge. The voices weave in and out in transparent and beautifully flowing lines of close harmony, creating at once the loveliest and most solemn moment in the act:

No. 8
Adagio

Act One, Scene 5

THE last scene of the first act brings us right into the castle of Don Giovanni, where there is apparently nothing going on but brilliant gaiety everywhere. No fewer than three separate orchestras are playing in as many little balconies of the main hall; two other rooms for dancing are observable on the sides; while in back, doors open onto the garden, which is also illuminated with lamps and gaily decorated.

The party is in full swing, with Don Giovanni and Leporello offering refreshments to everyone. Masetto and Zerlina are rather nervous—and with good reason, for the Don starts flirting with Zerlina almost at once. She cannot help responding a little; and as Masetto gets angrier and angrier, Leporello and the Don promise that he will be punished for his jealousy. The entrance of the three maskers temporarily puts a stop to the growing tension. They are cordially welcomed, and the Don calls for more music. As the Minuet is again struck up, he picks Zerlina for his partner; the maskers consult together; and Leporello pursues and annoys the jealous Masetto, finally forcing the poor fellow to dance with him.

The musical and dramatic effect here is extraordinarily ingenious when it is well done, but practically impossible to reproduce on a single piano. Mozart has three different dances going on at once, each of the stage orchestras playing a different tune in a different rhythm:

No. 9
Andantino

The minuet, on the top line, is for the nobles, the contradance for the peasants, and the waltz for Leporello and Masetto. In the general excitement the Don still pursues Zerlina, who tries (not too violently) to escape him, and finally he manages to draw her off to a room on the right. Masetto meanwhile has managed to shake off Leporello, who follows his master into the next room. A moment later, the dancing is interrupted by a cry from Zerlina off stage, and everyone turns to the door, which is locked. They try to force it and are about to break it down when the Don comes out, prodding Leporello in before him at the point of his sword (carefully kept in the scabbard).

No one is fooled. They all angrily attack their host, Don Ottavio even threatening him with a pistol. But in the general confusion of the exciting ensemble number that follows, Giovanni never once loses his coolness. His sword now drawn, he makes his way through the crowd and gets away from all of them through the window into the garden in back.

Act Two, Scene 1

THE second act starts with formulas that are already familiar. It is evening on a square in Seville with Donna Elvira's house and balcony on one side—though we are not told whose address it is till a little later on. Don Giovanni is arguing with Leporello on their pet theme: Leporello wants to leave this service, and the Don wants to keep him in it. A large tip—four doubloons (about sixteen dollars)—makes Leporello begin to see reason, provided the Don will only leave the women alone. "Give up the women?" cries the Don. "Why, they're more necessary to me than bread and breath!" As for what Leporello calls "deceiving," it is all done for love. How could one be faithful to just one woman without being cruel to all the others? No, the Don's expanse of sentiment is far too wide for any such niggardly ideas: he wishes well for all women.

And now to business. If Leporello will kindly lend the Don his costume, he'd like to try his luck with Donna Elvira's lovely little maid. And why the exchange of cloaks? Well, says the Don—possibly remembering Masetto and Zerlina—common folk sometimes have suspicions about the motives of noblemen; and, angrily silencing Leporello's protests, he exchanges hats and cloaks with him.

But it is Donna Elvira herself, and not the maid, who appears on the balcony, still breathing romantic revenge. The Don takes cruel advantage of the situation. He stands behind Leporello (who, in the dark of the night, can easily be mistaken for the Don) and with his own voice pleads to be taken back by Elvira. At the same time, he moves Leporello's arms for him in appropriately romantic gestures—a bit of low comedy that few actors can resist from overindulging to the extent of spoiling some very lovely music. The foolish Elvira succumbs almost at once, and after a trio, in which the Don and his servant laugh at her, she comes down to them. As she descends inside the house, the Don instructs the reluctant Leporello to impersonate him in the dark and persuade Elvira to leave with him so that the coast may be clear again for Giovanni's own love-making.

Leporello is at first afraid to try this deception, but he has no choice; and when he finds the job easier than he thought, with Elvira practically melting in his arms, he rather warms up to the business. He is swearing eternal fidelity when the Don, who has been watching on the side, jumps out and makes believe he is a holdup man about to kill them both. Elvira and Leporello run away.

Don Giovanni now sets the stage for himself—even to a mandolin that he had brought along and leant carefully against the side of the house. He picks up the instrument and, to a tune that he had already begun a few moments earlier when serenading Elvira, he now serenades her maid (see p. 44). He thinks he hears the girl coming onto the balcony; but just at this point a group of armed peasants, led by Masetto, come in, looking for the Don, whom they fully intend to murder. Seeing there are quite a few of them, Giovanni makes believe he is Leporello, disguising his voice just as skillfully as Leporello disguised his own when wooing Elvira. He tells the rustics that he fully agrees in their low opinion of Don Giovanni, and he instructs them how to find him: half must go this way, half the other way, and should they run across a man in such a cloak and such a hat (and here he describes the costume he had forced on poor Leporello), making love to a lady, that will be Don Giovanni. He gets the rest to leave, and Masetto to stay with him.

"Won't just a beating do for the Don?" he asks.

"No," says Masetto, "I want to kill him, to cut him up into a hundred pieces."

"Do you have good weapons?" asks the Don in friendly anxiety.

"Well, just look," says Masetto, and hands over his musket and pistol.

Whereupon the Don takes them from him, beats the poor fellow with the flat of his sword, and runs off. Masetto sets up a great cry, but Zerlina comes on the stage and discovers that he is not nearly so badly hurt as he thinks he is. She sings to him with Mozartean magic about the remedy she has for him —a most pleasant medicine that she carries with her. Doesn't he guess what it is? And she lays his hand on her heart as he hobbles off the stage with her, already half cured (see p. 48).

Act Two, Scene 2

IN THE next scene, Leporello and Donna Elvira have accidentally strayed into the garden of the Commandant, where Donna Anna lives. It is still dark; Elvira still thinks she is with Don Giovanni; and Donna Anna and Don Ottavio, who enter on the other side, are still busy mourning her father. While Donna Anna laments and Ottavio tries to comfort her, Leporello gropes along the wall for an exit. He thinks he has it, when he is suddenly confronted by Zerlina and Masetto. Everyone, of course, mistakes him for his master, whose clothes he is wearing, and they are about to murder him when Donna Elvira intervenes and pleads for "her husband," as she calls him. Leporello, in desperation, now shows his face. They are first astonished and then angrily determined to punish him too; but he has learned enough from his master to talk himself out of harder spots than this one. He kneels before them, apologizes to each in succession, blames the Don, pleads to be allowed to go, and suddenly darts out.

Don Ottavio now says he is sure that Don Giovanni is the murderer of the Commandant (though his reasoning is not quite clear), and he will go and get some help from the law. For a Spanish don, this would appear to be a sin against romantic tradition, but he makes up for it by singing one of the loveliest arias Mozart ever wrote—the fluent and enormously difficult *"Il mio tesoro"* (see p. 53).

(A low-comedy scene follows in the score, but it is almost always omitted in modern productions. Zerlina catches up with Leporello once more, drags him around the stage, ties him up in a chair, threatens him with a razor, and then goes off for the others. While they are gone, the window to which Zerlina had tied the rope drops, and she returns with the others to find that Leporello has hopped out. I have never seen this scene done, but I have no deep regrets about it. This scene is followed by the aria *"Mi tardi,"* in which Donna Elvira once again voices her grief over Don Giovanni's betrayal of her. It is a very fine aria and in American productions usually is sung before a drop curtain.)

Act Two, Scene 3

IT IS now two o'clock in the morning, as Don Giovanni tells us in the next scene. Still in Leporello's cloak, he has just climbed over the wall of a churchyard whose chief ornament is a large equestrian statue of the Commandant. The Don is in high spirits, wondering what has happened to Leporello and rubbing his hands over another little adventure he has had in the meantime. Leporello, escaping from his tormentors, comes the same way, but he is naturally in poorer spirits. Those spirits are not improved by the little tale the Don tells. He had met a pretty little miss in the street, made up to her, and been very tenderly received because—and here's the joke—she mistook the Don for Leporello himself. It was one of Leporello's girls.

"But suppose she had been my wife?" objects the servant.

"All the better," laughs the Don.

Just then the moon breaks through the clouds, the statue is flooded with a ghostly light, and a voice solemnly says, "Your joking will end before dawn."

For a moment the Don thinks it must be someone hiding in the churchyard. Then the voice speaks again, and he suspects it may be the statue. He forces the terror-stricken Leporello to read the inscription on the base. This is what it says:

Here I wait for Vengeance on the Impious Man who Killed Me.

Leporello can scarcely read for fright, but the Don apparently remains unmoved. He calls it a great joke and instructs Leporello to invite the statue to dinner. Poor Leporello does his best to get out of this impiety, and only after a few threats of sudden death at the end of the Don's sword does he manage to sputter out the invitation—adding that this is strictly the Don's invitation, not his own. Leporello sees the statue nod its head in acceptance and reports the phenomenon to his master. Finally the Don sees it too, but he insists that the statue should answer his invitation orally. It does, with one "Yes."

The Don still tries to appear unafraid. He remarks that this is certainly bizarre and instructs Leporello to get ready to receive their guest. But his voice (the passage is marked *mezza voce*) shows that he is moved underneath his cold exterior. As for Leporello, he can hardly stand for fright, and he makes no bones about saying so as he runs off.

Act Two, Scene 4

IN THE brief scene that follows, Don Ottavio tries to persuade Donna Anna to forget her sorrow, now that Don Giovanni will soon be brought to justice, and to marry him. In an aria full of tenderness—and also of difficult, florid passages—Donna Anna tells him that she cannot do so now, while her sorrow is still fresh, but that she loves him and some day heaven will bless their union. This is the famous *"Non mi dir"* (see p. 58).

Act Two, Scene 5

THE last scene of all—and the most dramatic—takes place in Don Giovanni's banqueting hall, which is brightly lighted, richly furnished, and blessed with a private orchestra that plays in a gallery. The tunes it plays include some of the hits of Mozart's day—an air each from Martín y Soler's *Una Cosa Rara*, Sarti's *Fra Due Litiganti*, and Mozart's own *Le Nozze di Figaro*, which was an enormous hit in Prague at the time of the *première* of *Don Giovanni*. Leporello comments on this last (it is the *"Non più andraï"*) with: "I know that thing only too well."

Meantime, the Don is eating away, served dish after dish by his dining-room staff, and calling on Leporello to amuse him. Just as the meal is about over, Donna Elvira rushes in in a frenzied mood and begs the Don to change his manner of living. Giovanni thinks this is a good joke, mockingly kneels beside her, and makes fun of her while Leporello marvels at the lady's persistence. No one seems to notice the sound of approaching thunder. When the Don has had enough of his joke, he sits down again to eat—and that is more than even the long-suffering Elvira can stand. She curses him and starts to rush out of the center door in back.

At once, she jumps back and screams. Leporello follows her and, just outside the door, also lets out a shout. He comes back to report in quaking accents that the white stone man is there. Don Giovanni refuses to believe him, and when a knocking begins at the door, he orders Leporello to open. The poor fellow just can't do it: he can barely stand for fright, and he hides under the table.

The Don himself takes up a light, opens the door, and there stands the great marble figure of the statue, announcing—to the accompaniment of thunder and the music of No. 1—that he has come to dinner, as he was invited to. Still the perfect gentleman, Don Giovanni orders Leporello to lay another cover, but the statue saves him this trouble. "Whoever has eaten in heaven," he says, "does not need earthly food." On the contrary, he has come to invite the Don to dine with him. Does he accept?

Leporello, still under the table, begs his master not to accept and even tries to assure the statue that there's a previous engagement which will interfere. But the Don, protesting—perhaps too much—that he doesn't even know the meaning of fear, accepts the invitation, if not exactly with pleasure. At once, the statue reaches out his hand to seal the compact, and Don Giovanni finds himself held in a terrible stony clasp.

The statue urges him—even at this late hour—to repent, but the Don proudly refuses and orders his guest away. Finally, he wrests his hand free as the statue, in deep tones, tells him his time is up.

Flames start leaping up everywhere, a chorus of hollow voices announces the Don's eternal damnation, and he himself at last cries out in agony as fire consumes the whole house.*

---

*In Europe many opera houses end *Don Giovanni* at this point. They fear that what follows will be an anticlimax. Mozart apparently wanted only to lower the tragic tone of the previous action and to point the moral to his tale.

The curtain goes down on this scene of destruction, and before it step Elvira, Anna, Zerlina, Ottavio, and Masetto, accompanied by the ministers of justice, whose job has been anticipated for them. Leporello, who somehow has managed to escape the conflagration, comes in and, still all but incoherent with fright, tells what he has seen. Anna then promises to marry Ottavio after a year of mourning; Zerlina and Masetto plan prompter nuptials; while Elvira declares she will enter a convent, and Leporello that he will seek a better master.

And the opera closes on a moral little sextet in which all agree that Don Giovanni has come to a most appropriate end.

Give Me Your Hand, Zerlina

LÀ CI DAREM LA MANO

Andante   Original key: A

DON GIOVANNI

Give me your hand, Zer - li - na,   An-swer your lov-er's plea;
Là ci da-rem la ma-no,   *là mi di-rai di sì;*

ZERLINA

Yours to com-mand, Zer - li - na,   If you_ would care for_ me.   I
ve - di, non è lon - ta - no,   *par - tiam,_ ben_ mio, da_ qui.*   *Vor-*

care, and yet I care not   For what may be in store,   I
rei, e non vor - re - i, mi tre - ma un po - co il cor, fe-

Ah, yes, there's no de - fy - ing,___ A love be - yond de - ny - ing___ For
An - diam, an - diam, mio be - ne,___ a ri - sto - rar le pe - ne___ d'un'

love must___ have its___ way! A-
in - no - cen - te a - mor! An-

way with all mis - giv - ing,___ For life was made for liv - ing;___ True
diam, an - diam, mio be - ne,___ a ri - sto - rar le pe - ne___ d'un'

love is ours to - day! My
in - no - cen - te a - mor! An -

DON GIOVANNI

She Is the Measure

DALLA SUA PACE

Original key: G

Andante

DON OTTAVIO

She is the meas-ure Of all my
Dal - la sua pa - ce la mia di -

glad - ness, What gives her pleas - ure Dis - pels my
pen - de, quel che a lei pia - ce vi - ta mi

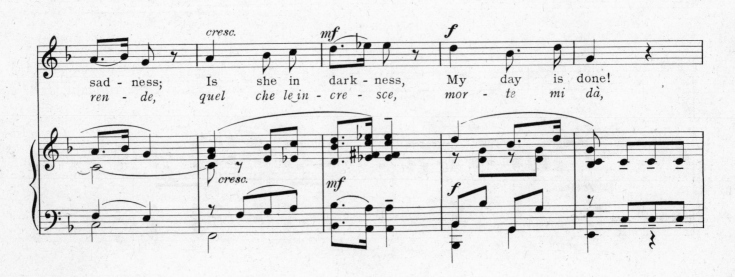

cresc. *mf* *f*

sad - ness; Is she in dark - ness, My day is done!
ren - de, quel che le in - cre - sce, mor - te mi dà,

My_____ light, my light is gone!
mor - - - te, mor - te mi dà.

When_she is weep - ing, I weep_ be-
S'el - la so - spi - ra, so - spi - ro an-

side her; A - wake or sleep - ing What-
ch'i - o, è mia quell' i - ra, quel

e'er be - tide her, There is no_ good - ness
pian - - to è mi - o; e non ho_ be - ne,

If she has___ none; There is___ no___
s'el - la non___ l'ha,

heav - en, If she has none,___ There is___ no___
be - ne, s'el - la non l'ha,___ e non___ ho___

hap - pi - ness, If she has none!_____ She is the
be - ne, s'el - la non l'ha!_____ Dal - la sua

meas - ure Of all___ my___ glad - - ness,
pa - ce Of la mia___ di - pen - - de,

sad - ness,_____ Is she in dark - ness, My day is done,
ren - de,_____ quel che le in - cre - sce, mor - te mi dà,

My_____ light, my light is gone!
mor - - - te, mor - te mi dà,

My day is done, is she in dark - ness,_____ My light is
mor - te mi dà, quel che le in - cre - sce,_____ mor - te mi

(Melody)

gone!
dà!

Let's Have a Party

FINCH' HAN DAL VINO

Though I have kissed a few, I may have missed a few,
Ah, la mia li - sta do - man mat - ti - na

There's al-ways room for one la - dy more!
d'u - na de - ci - na de - viau-men - tar.

When I have had ___ more,
Ah, la mia li - sta

Then I can add more names to the score.
d'u - na de - ci - na de - viau-men - tar.

Look on the high - ways, search all the by - ways,
Se tro-vi in piaz - za qual - che ra - gaz - za,

Gath - er the la - dies, get me a score!
te - co an-cor quel - la cer - ca me - nar.

Though I have had a few, still I can
Ah, la mia li - sta do - man mat -

add a few, There's al-ways room for one doz - en more!
ti - na d'u - na de - ci - na de - vi au-men - tar.

Beat Me, Beat Me

BATTI, BATTI

Original key: F

Beat me, beat me, dear Ma - set - to, beat your
Bat - ti, bat - ti,o bel Ma - set - to, la tua

poor de - spised Zer - li - na; Here am I, a will - ing
po - ve - ra Zer - li - na; sta - rò qui come a - gnel -

vic - tim, Beat me till I can - not stand!
li - na le tue bot - te ad a - spet - tar.

) 35 (

Beat me, beat me, your poor Zer - li - na; Here am
Bat - ti, bat - ti la tua Zer - li - na; sta - rò

I,_____ here am I,_____ Beat me till__ I can - not
qui,_____ sta - rò qui_____ le tue bot - te ad_ a - spet -

stand!
tar.

Beat me till your fin - gers wear out!
La - scie - rò stra-ziar-mi il cri - ne,

) 36 (

I will let you tear my hair out! Then_ when_
La scie - rò ca - var - mi gli_occhi, e_ le_

you_ are quite,_ quite_ through,_ Oh then_ I'll_ kiss_ your dar - ling_
ca - re tue_ ma - ni - ne lie - ta_ poi sa - prò ba -

hand,_ I'll kiss_ your hand, _ Ah,
ciar,_ sa - prò_ ba - ciar, _ ba -

yes _ I'll kiss_ your dar - - ling_
ciar, _ sa - prò,_ sa - prò_ ba -

hand.
ciar.

Beat me, Bat - ti,

beat me, dear Ma - set - to, beat your poor de - spised Zer-
bat - ti, o bel Ma - set - to, la tua po - ve - ra Zer-

li - na; Here am I, a will - ing vic - tim, Beat me,
li - na; sta - rò qui co - me a - gnel - li - na le tue

till I can - not stand! My dear Ma - set - to!
bot - te ad a - spet - tar. O bel Ma - set - to!

Beat me, beat me, Here am I, _____ close at hand, _____ beat me
Bat - ti, bat - ti! sta - rò qui, _____ sta - rò qui _____ le tue

till_ I_ can - not stand.
bot-te ad_ a - spet-tar.

Don't you dare to?
Ah, lo ve - do,

Can't you bear_ to?
non hai co - re,

You do not
ah, non hai

cresc.

dare_ to, do_ not care_ to, can - not bear to!
co - re, ah, _____ lo ve - do, non_ hai co - re.

cresc.

f

Minuet

Serenade

DEH VIENI ALLA FINESTRA

Original key

heart   To   hear my lone - ly sighs!
lar   il   pian - to mi   o.

If you re - fuse___ the
Se   ne - ghi a me___ di

songs   that   all be - long___ to you,   I'll
dar   qual - che ri - sto - ro,   da -

die   of hap - less love,   Be - fore___ your cru - el___
van - ti ag - li oc - chi tuoi   mo - rir___ vo - gl'i -

eyes!
o!

The
Tu

hon — ey of your kiss — es Sweet — ens my
ch'hai la boc - ca dol - ce più che il

quasi Mandolino

ben legato
Melody

very short

song for you, Ah, the thought of your
mie — le, tu che il zuc - che - ro

beau - ty fills all my heart with pain.
por - ti in mez - zo al co - re.

) 46 (

I pray you, come___ and
Non es - ser, gio - ja

hear how much I long___ for you;
mia, con me cru-de - le!

O - pen your heart___ to love, and I___ shall live a-
La - scia-ti al - men___ ve - der, mio bell'___ a - mo -

gain!
re!

I Have a Cure for You

VEDRAI, CARINO

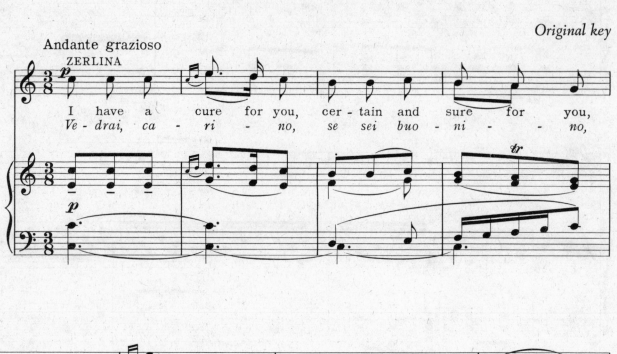

I have a cure for you, cer-tain and sure for you,
Ve-drai, ca-ri - no, se sei buo-ni - no,

I have a rem - e-dy, let us pro - ceed.
che bel ri - me-di-o ti vo-glio dar!

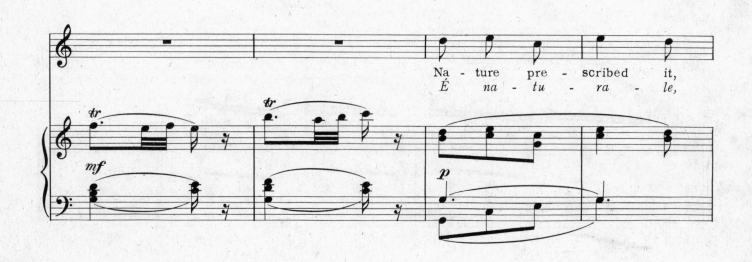

Na - ture pre - scribed it,
É na - tu - ra - le,

When you've im - bibed it,
non dà di - sgu - sto,

You will a - gree,___ it's just what you need, Oh,
e lo spe - zia - le non lo sa far, no,

just what you need, Oh, let us pro - ceed.___
non lo sa far, no, non lo sa far.___

Mil - lions have used___ it, None has re - fused___ it,
È un cer - to bal - sa - mo che por - to ad - dos - so,

If you can take____ it, I'll do the rest.____
*da - re t'el pos - so, se il vuoi pro - var.*____

What is this po - tion?
Sa - per vor - re - sti

Have you no no - tion, O dar - ling have - n't you
do - ve mi sta, do - ve, do - ve, do - ve mi

guessed?____
*sta?*____

p   *legato*

Here is this heart of mine,
Sen - ti - lo bat - te - re,

Give me your hand, Feel how it beats for you, What it re-
toc - ca - mi quà, sen - ti - lo bat - te - re, sen - ti - lo

peats for you. You'll un - der-
bat - te - re, toc - ca - mi

stand, Hear what it tells to you, Hear what it spells to you.
quà! Sen - ti - lo bat - te - re, sen - ti - lo bat - te - re,

(Places his hand over her heart.)

Tell - ing you, com - pel - ling you, Give me your hand,___ your___ hand!___ Feel_ how_ it's_ beat - ing_ and_ what it's re - peat - ing, Feel how it's beat - ing, Give me your hand___ and you'll_ un - der - stand.

sen - ti - lo___ bat - te - re,___ toc - ca - mi quà!___ quà!___ quà!___ sen - ti - lo___ bat - te - re, __ toc - ca - mi quà, quà! toc - ca - mi quà, quà! toc - ca - mi quà,___ quà, toc - ca - mi quà!

Take My Beloved
IL MIO TESORO

Andante grazioso

Original key: B-flat

DON OTTAVIO

p

Take my be-lov-ed in your keep - ing,
Con - sole ___ her, and

Il mio te-so-ro in tan - to
an - da - te, an -

sempre poco Ped.   *sempre legato*

drive ___ a - way her fears.
Bid her for-get her

da - - te a con - so - lar!
E del bel ci-glio il

sempre legato

weep - ing, and help her dry her tears, ___
Con - sole ___ her, con -

pian - to cer - ca - te di a - sciu - gar, ___
cer - ca - te, cer -

sole___ her, and help___ her dry her tears,___ To___
ca - te, cer - ca - - te dia - -sciu - gar,___ cer -

dry_____
ca - - - - - - - - - te___

her tears. Tell her that I must leave her,
dia - sciu - gar. Di - te - le, che i suoi tor - ti

Tell her I shall a - venge her, Tell_____ her I shall___ a -
a ven - di - car io va - do, a_____ ven - di - car___ io___

venge her.
va - do.
I'll right
Che sol
the wrongs
di stra -
that
gie

grieve her,
mor - ti
Then
nun -
when my_ task
zio vo - glio
is
tor -

done,
nar
tell
nun -
her, we shall_ be_ one,
zio vo - gl'io_ tor - nar,
yes,
si,

tell her we shall_ be_ one!_ Ah!
nun - zio vo - gl'io_ tor - nar!_ Ah!

) 55 (

Take my be-lov-ed in your keep - ing,
Il mio te-so—ro in-tan-to

Con - sole——— her and drive———
An - da - te, an - da - - -

- a - way her fears.
-te a— con - so - lar!

Bid her for - get her
e del— bel— ci - glio il

sempre legato

weep - ing, and help her dry her tears, _____ Con-
pian - to cer - ca - te di a - sciu - gar _____ cer -

sole _____ her, con - sole _____ her And help _____ her dry _____ her
ca - te, cer - ca - te, cer - ca - te di a _____ sciu -

tears, _____ to dry _____
gar, _____ cer - ca - - - - - - - - - -

- - te _____ di a - sciu - gar.
                    her tears.

Ah, Dear Heart

NON MI DIR

Original key: F

aid___ me;   You must   know my heart_____ is__   true;___
ma - i,   tu   co - no - sci la_____ mia_   fè,___

You_____   should___   know___   my_heart   is__   true.
tu_____   co -   no -   sci_ la   mia_   fè.

Love   must
Cal - ma,

wait   un - til___ the___   mor - row,
cal - ma il_ tuo___   tor - men - to,

Love must wait up-on my sor - row, Love must
Se di duol non vuoi ch'io mo - ra, se di

wait up - on my sor - row un - til the mor - row.
duol non vuoi ch'io mo - ra, non vuoi ch'io mo - ra.

cresc.
f

Ah, dear heart do not up - braid me,
Non mi dir, bell' i - dol mi - o,

p

Ah, be - lieve me My heart is true.
che son i - o cru - del con te.

mf   sf   p

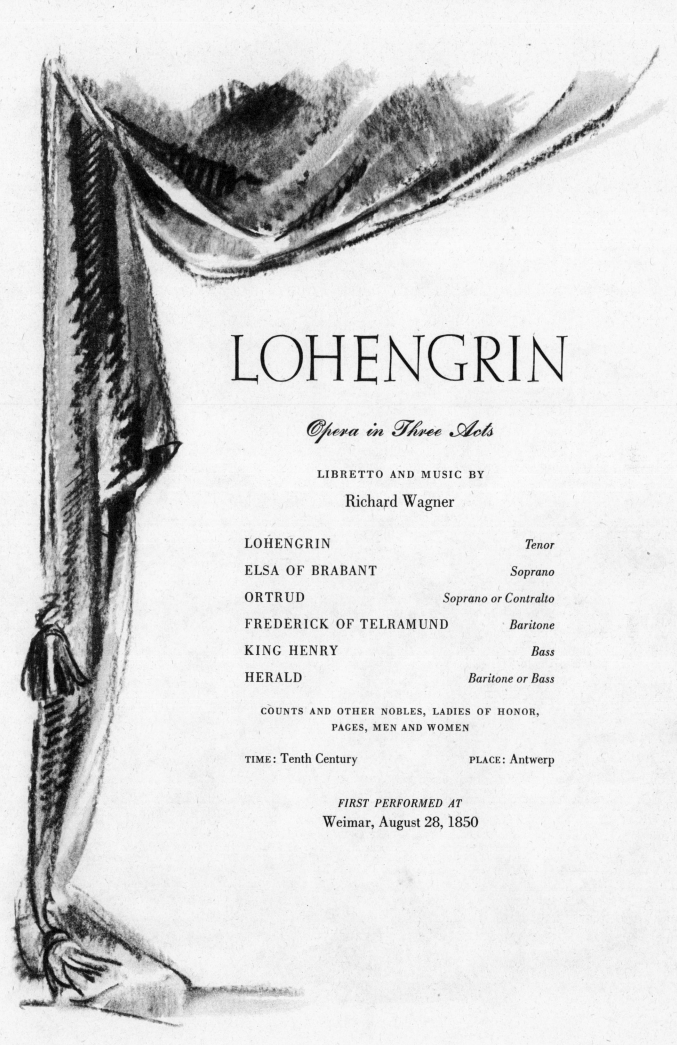

LOHENGRIN

Opera in Three Acts

LIBRETTO AND MUSIC BY

Richard Wagner

LOHENGRIN	*Tenor*
ELSA OF BRABANT	*Soprano*
ORTRUD	*Soprano or Contralto*
FREDERICK OF TELRAMUND	*Baritone*
KING HENRY	*Bass*
HERALD	*Baritone or Bass*

COUNTS AND OTHER NOBLES, LADIES OF HONOR,
PAGES, MEN AND WOMEN

TIME: Tenth Century   PLACE: Antwerp

FIRST PERFORMED AT
Weimar, August 28, 1850

Lohengrin

RICHARD WAGNER

BY MODERN standards of morals and of realism, the characters of Lohengrin and Elsa in Wagner's libretto appear to be both incredible and unpleasant. It is difficult to see Lohengrin as anything but priggish and unsporting, while Elsa seems to be unusually weak and simple-minded even for an operatic heroine. The casual operagoer has no way of knowing that these characters are not to be judged by modern standards, that the story and the symbolism are based on ancient folk tales, that Lohengrin is the embodiment of the abstract force for good and Elsa of maidenly purity and love, that the whole business about the hiding of Lohengrin's name harks back to an almost universal primitive belief concerning the power for evil that resides in the knowledge of a name.

The leading baritone role in *Tannhäuser*, the Wagnerian opera that preceded *Lohengrin*, is that of Wolfram von Eschenbach, an historical knight and poet who died in the early thirteenth century. This Wolfram, acclaimed the greatest poet of his time (although he himself once said that he was illiterate), composed the earliest known poem on the subject of Lohengrin, and Wagner must have read it. There are, however, several other medieval versions of the story, and Wagner, borrowing from all of them, relied chiefly on a later one called the *Wartburgkrieg*.

This long, anonymous poem will be recognized by Wagnerians as the source of part of the second act of *Tannhäuser*; but two-thirds of it concerns the adventures of the Swan Knight, Lohengrin. At the Wartburg, in the court of Landgraf Hermann of Thuringia, Wolfram competes as a poet not only with Tannhäuser but also with an evil character named Klingsor, whom Wagner later resurrected in *Parsifal*. The adventures of Lohengrin are put into Wolfram's mouth; and so it happens that a baritone from one of Wagner's operas supplies the material for another.

As a matter of record, Wagner had considered Lohengrin as a subject for an opera several years before he completed *Tannhäuser* in April, 1845. During that summer, on a vacation in Bohemia, he reread the old epic, and nothing, not even his doctor's advice, could keep him from sketching it out as a possible libretto. He himself records that the struggle against starting to work on it was lost one day while he was performing his midday ablutions. "Unable to remain in the bath for the prescribed hour," he wrote, "I impatiently jumped out after a few minutes and, barely giving myself time to dress, ran home like a madman to put down on paper what was crying for expression within me."

What was crying for expression within him turned out to be the most dramatically sound and the most popular tragic opera he ever composed. It was also a considerable refinement on the sources he had been digesting for the past few years. One example will serve to show how he altered the details of a poem that is crude at best and—to quote Wagner's own word for it—"mawkish" in other places. The duel between Lohengrin and Telramund in the first act of the opera is a simple exchange of blows, with Telramund quickly falling before the supernatural powers of the Swan Knight, who magnanimously grants him his life. In the *Wartburgkrieg*, the fight goes on for some time. When Telramund refuses to admit defeat, Lohengrin "squeezes him in blind fury until his ribs crack and the blood bursts from his mouth. He picks him up and hurls him to the ground with a resounding crash; he strikes the helmet from his enemy's head and stabs at his hands with his dagger." Finally, after a few more squeezes, poor Telramund is just able to say he has had enough, whereupon he is promptly led off by the executioner and beheaded.

It is as a folk tale, then, that we should understand the story of *Lohengrin*. Wagner, however, made it somewhat difficult to take it simply that way by including in the story not only a real historical figure, Henry I of Germany (who also appeared in the *Wartburgkrieg*), but also a new character, Ortrud, who, by her force and credibility, dominates a large part of the action. An old French version of the Lohengrin legend mentions a Duchess of Cleve who questions the origins of the

Swan Knight. With not much more suggestion than that, Wagner made her an understandable woman, a sort of career woman with acute intelligence, executive capacity, and courage. It was the sort of woman Wagner professed a loathing for, and accordingly he made Ortrud a devotee of heathen gods and a sorceress while the good people in the cast are all Christians. So real does the wicked Ortrud become that it would be difficult to take the swan and the Holy Grail references seriously were they not presented in such pervasively convincing musical dress.

Musically, *Lohengrin* marks the end and the culmination of Wagner's earlier work. In it he thoroughly developed the leitmotiv system,* but he had not yet achieved his ideal of a constant flow of melody with no breaks between set numbers. *Lohengrin* is full of set numbers, and the voice is melodically more important than it is in his later operas. That may be one reason for its being generally more popular than the later operas and for thoroughgoing Wagnerians' regarding it with the patronizing affection some parents reserve for their defective children.

As was his custom, Wagner wrote the libretto first. He then had to wait a year before he could begin composing the music. He started with the third act, continued with the first, and ended with the second. Then he orchestrated all of it, finishing in 1848. But by that time he was deeply involved in revolutionary political activities in Dresden, where he was conductor of the opera, and the following year he had to leave Germany as a political refugee.

So it happened that the *première* of the opera took place in the composer's absence. Wagner did not hear it till over ten years later when, as he said, it had become so successful that he was himself pretty nearly the only German who had not heard it performed.

That *première* took place in the little city of Weimar, August 28, 1850. The first performance was no great success, and it is hard to see how it could have been. Liszt, whose enthusiasm was responsible for the work's being performed at all, conducted, and he was never very much of a professional with the baton. His orchestra boasted only five first violins and six second, the whole numbering fewer than forty. The chorus was no larger, and there were no singers of the first rank in Weimar. It is, of course, remarkable that a town like Weimar, with a population of some ten thousand, should have had an opera house at all; but thanks to a music-loving ruler it did, and it produced opera regularly. Nevertheless, the standards of singing and playing in Germany a century ago were pitifully low compared with modern ones; and the most remarkable part of the story is that so difficult a work as *Lohengrin* should have survived its earliest performances and become a staple part of the operatic repertoire.

The reasons for *Lohengrin's* popularity are not hard to find. Despite the inconsistencies mentioned above, the telling of the story is a model of clarity in its main outlines; while a mere reading of the libretto makes some of the more static passages, like the beginning of the second act, highly dramatic. Far more important than the dramaturgy is the dramatic impact of the score. It is full of good set numbers, like the Preludes to Acts I and III, "Elsa's Prayer," the "Bridal Chorus," and "Lohengrin's Narrative," all of them popular in concert form. When given on the stage, however, in their dramatic setting, the impact is enormously enhanced, especially when some familiarity with the music of the whole opera makes clear the significance of the principal leitmotivs. Add to this the consummate artistry of Wagner's orchestral coloration, the contrasts in striking stage pictures, and the possibilities for pleasing eye pictures (unfortunately not often realized), and it is not hard to see why *Lohengrin* has had more performances at the Metropolitan than any other opera excepting only *Aïda*.

Prelude

THIS is the way Wagner himself described the Prelude to *Lohengrin:* "Out of the clear blue ether of the sky there seems to condense a wonderful yet at first hardly perceptible vision; and out of this there gradually emerges, ever more and more clearly, an angel host bearing in its midst the sacred Grail. As it approaches earth, it pours out exquisite odors, like streams of gold, ravishing the senses of the beholder. The glory of the vision grows and grows until it seems as if the rapture must be shattered and dispersed by the very vehemence of its own expansion.

"The vision draws nearer, and the climax is reached when at last the Grail is revealed in all its glorious reality, radiating fiery beams and shaking the soul with emotion. The beholder sinks on his knees in adoring self-annihilation. The Grail pours out its light on him like a benediction, and consecrates

*Analysts have discovered no fewer than forty-two leitmotivs in *Lohengrin,* the more important of which are quoted and named in the description of the opera which follows.

him to its service; then the flames gradually die away, and the angel host soars up again to the ethereal heights in tender joy, having made pure once more the hearts of men by the sacred blessing of the Grail."

The Prelude (see p. 75) begins with six tonic chords in A major high up in the violins and flutes, and so soft they can hardly be heard. (In opera houses where latecomers are seated during the Prelude, you seldom hear the very beginning at all: you just know it is going on because the conductor is waving his baton.) Then the violins alone, firsts and seconds each divided into four parts, give out the motive of the Holy Grail:

No. 1
Adagio

(The chords marked *a* in the second bar of this motive also serve as the Swan motive.)

Gradually other instruments are added—first flutes, oboes, and clarinets, later the lower strings, horns, bassoons, and contrabassoon. The instrumentation and harmonization grow richer and richer as the Grail theme appears in these lower wind instruments with a syncopated countermelody in the violins. Finally the climax comes with the trumpets and trombones spreading out a great crescendo on the same theme, the entire orchestra joining in *fortissimo*, and the cymbals crashing, "radiating fiery beams and shaking the soul with emotion."

It all fades away then on a beautiful descending scale that has been variously called the "Lament for Separation" and the "Farewell of the Angels."

No. 2
Adagio

Down it comes from the heights—and the Prelude fades into nothingness, as it had begun, with the violins alone softly breathing a part of the Grail theme.

Act One

THE first act of *Lohengrin* is a little drama complete in itself with beginning, middle, and end—a happy end. It takes place on the banks of the Scheldt River near Antwerp in the early part of the tenth century, where Henry the Fowler has come with a small army of Saxon nobles to ask the assistance of the Brabantines in the impending war against the Hungarians. As the curtain rises on a great crescendo, the King is revealed, seated on an eminence, beneath the judgment oak surrounded by his Saxon retinue. The Brabantine lords stand across the stage on his right, with Count Frederick of Telramund and his wife Ortrud at their head.

The royal Herald signals for trumpeters on the stage, who blow the royal summons:

No. 3
Allegro

Then, in stiff, clipped, baritone accents the Herald announces that the King of Germany has come on affairs of state: do the Brabantines acknowledge him as their liege lord? Striking their swords across their shields, the Brabantines do so. Once more the trumpeters sound the royal summons, and Henry rises. In a rather long statement, that is usually cut on the American stage, he gives a report on the military state of the nation: a nine-year truce with Hungary is over, and it is time to resist the Eastern hordes again. The Saxon nobles briefly echo his warlike sentiments.

Henry now seats himself and in a more somber vein says that he has come to bid the Brabantines to join him at Mayence, but he finds the country in a turmoil. Will Frederick, Count of Telramund, a knight of good name, kindly explain what it is all about?

Solemnly, to the first measures of the Accusation motive:

No. 4
Andante moderato

Telramund steps forward, thanks the King for coming for judgment, swears to tell the truth, and begins his story. When the Duke of Brabant died some time ago, he appointed Telramund the guardian of his two children, Elsa and Godfrey —a trust faithfully carried out. One day, however (and here the music depicts Telramund's growing excitement), Elsa came back from a walk in the woods with her young brother and claimed that she could not find him. No other searcher could find him either; and when Telramund questioned Elsa, her paleness and trembling betrayed her guilt. At least, that is what Telramund says. He was filled with a loathing for her now; he gladly renounced the right, given by the old Duke of Brabant, to Elsa's hand, and took a bride more to his liking. Here he presents Ortrud to the King, and they solemnly bow to each other. Then Telramund steps determinedly forward and makes his formal accusation: Elsa, he says, is guilty of fratricide, wherefore he claims the right of rulership in Brabant, both because he was the old Duke's nearest of kin and because his wife, Ortrud, daughter of the Prince of Friesland, comes of a race that once ruled here too. "Thou hearest the charge, O King," he ends. "Deliver judgment."

So grave a charge shocks these medieval knights, and the King can scarcely believe it. The excitable Telramund feels it necessary now to back up his charges by finding a motive for the crime, and in doing so is guilty of an inconsistency (which no one on the stage notes) that should warn us that his case is weak. (As a matter of fact, as we learn later on, his more intelligent and forceful wife had made the story up out of whole cloth. Telramund just hadn't learned his lesson very well.) He says now that the dreamy Elsa had refused his offer of marriage—which should put a different complexion on the matter—and that she had hoped that by killing her brother she could deliver the dukedom to a secret lover she had.

This is too much for the King. He stops Telramund with a sharp gesture and asks that the accused be brought forward so that the trial can begin. The royal summons is sounded once more (No. 3); and as a sign that the court is in session, so to speak, the Kings hangs his shield on the judgment oak and swears not to use it until a verdict has been rendered. The Saxon nobles thrust their swords into the earth, the Brabantines lay theirs on the ground, echoing the King's oath, and the Herald calls upon Elsa to appear.

The entrance Elsa makes is highly effective both musically and dramatically. It is accompanied by the introduction of the Innocence theme played here and the half-dozen other

No. 5
Andante moderato

times it appears in the opera entirely by the wood-winds. The tone color suggests purity, and Wagner uses the wood-winds alone almost every time Elsa is introduced on the stage.

She comes in, hands folded, dressed all in white, her blonde hair hanging down in braids, and accompanied by a group of ladies in waiting similarly clothed and keeping a discreet distance. Through forty-four slow bars of music, she does not say a word; but first the men marvel that anyone appearing so pure can be accused of such a crime. The King asks whether she is indeed Elsa of Brabant, to which she nods assent. She nods again when he asks whether she recognizes him as her judge; and when he asks whether she knows the charge, she gives Telramund and Ortrud a shuddering glance. What answer does she make? asks the King, and with a gesture she says: Nothing. "Then you admit your guilt?" asks Henry once more, and Elsa murmurs her first words as though speaking to herself: "My poor brother!" Once more the King urges her to speak, and she begins her famous aria, "Elsa's Dream" (see p. 79).

Still half dreaming, she tells of how she prayed sorrowfully to God, gave out a heartfelt cry which echoed back faintly to her own ears, and was overcome by sleep. Once more the men express their wonder, and the King urges her to defend herself. Her expression changes from that of a dreamlike trance to an other-worldly confidence as the violins play the theme of the Holy Grail (No. 1). In this dream, she says, there came to her the most wonderful knight she had ever seen, dressed in shining armor, a golden horn slung over his shoulder and himself leaning on his sword. He seemed to step right out of the air. This description is accompanied by the Lohengrin motive:

No. 6
Animato

And then, in a broad melody that modulates practically in every other bar to a new key, and yet seems like the most natural progression in the world, she tells how he offered her consolation. He, she says (singing the second part of the Innocence theme), shall be her defender.

The men, deeply moved, take up Elsa's melody, and the King asks Telramund to reconsider his charges. Telramund, however, says he will have no truck with this dreamy nonsense. "See," he adds, "she talks about her lover." Furthermore, he has proof of her crime, but he is too proud to bring on his witness. He would rather, in the good old medieval manner, prove his accusation by the might of the sword. Will anyone take up the challenge? "No!" cry the Brabantines. "We fight only on your side." And as for the King, resumes Telramund, let him remember how well he had served him in the war against the Danes. This tenth-century identification of martial valor with truth-telling is immediately acknowledged by Henry, who says that he does not need to be reminded of Telramund's services: there is no more trustworthy knight. There remains, then, only to let God decide the issue through trial by combat, and the brasses trumpet out the Trial by Combat motive as Henry symbolically thrusts his sword into the earth before him:

No. 7
Allegro moderato

First he formally asks Telramund whether he will abide by such a decision, and he gets, of course, a strong affirmative. He turns to Elsa with the same question, and she also assents. But what champion does she have? ("Now we'll get the name of her lover!" interjects Telramund.) Elsa, still in a faraway mood, says it will be the knight who had come to console her; and with rising ecstasy, she adds the reward she has to offer him—her father's ducal crown. Then if he should think her worthy, she would be proud to become his wife.

The King takes her at her word, and the four trumpeters sound the royal summons once again. The Herald then, unaccompanied, calls in stentorian tones for the champion of Elsa of Brabant to appear. Four pizzicato chords in the orchestra are the only reply he gets. Elsa begins to grow uneasy, and Telramund begins to gloat. She then begs the King to have her knight called once more. "Perhaps," she says naïvely, "he is pretty far away and can't hear."

Again the trumpets, again the Herald, this time in a slightly higher key; but again there is only silence. Now Elsa falls to her knees and prays to God to send her hero once more in the time of her need. Her ladies in waiting pray with her in close harmony, but Elsa's voice rises above all in her ecstasy, and at the close of the prayer the Lohengrin motive (No. 6) is heard softly but unmistakably, played by the trumpets.

As Wagner planned it, Lohengrin was supposed to be seen in the distance coming in his swan-drawn boat up the river, the chorus of men excitedly reporting the marvel, answering each other back and forth in a growing crescendo as more and more caught sight of him. Then Lohengrin was to disappear behind a bend, and finally reappear at the back of the stage, in shining armor, with his horn at his side and leaning on his sword just as Elsa had described him. The first vision, however, is usually omitted as impracticable,* and Lohengrin's entrance is a visual disappointment because he is quickly shoved on in his boat, and only those seated in the center of the house can see what is happening because the chorus men stand in the way on both sides. The music, however, has a confused excitement, and Elsa stays on her knees in the foreground, not daring to look back. A grand climax

---

*When it is given on the larger German stages, the effect of distance is achieved by first showing a small child dressed like Lohengrin in a small boat. The tenor himself, in a larger boat, comes on the second time.

of welcome to the strange knight works up, at the end of which Lohengrin makes his first move to leave the boat. Silence falls on everyone as the violins breathe the motive of the Grail (No. 1).

With one foot still in the boat, Lohengrin bows toward the swan and, his back to the stage, sings it a soft farewell (see p. 85). At its close, on the words *"Leb' wohl!"* the swan should turn the boat around (but it usually doesn't) and swim away up the stream.

The entire assemblage (excepting, of course, Telramund and Ortrud) is filled with a deep awe expressed in a warm and tender chorus. The effect is achieved partly by keeping the melody low in the altos. Lohengrin meanwhile comes slowly forward and with great dignity bows to King Henry, hailing him with wishes for his success and fame. The King thanks him and adds that he thinks it must be God who sent the knight.

"I have come to fight for a maiden accused of a serious crime. Now let me see whether I am right in coming," says Lohengrin. He then addresses himself directly to Elsa, who, still half in a trance, throws herself at his feet. Will she, if he acts as her champion, put aside all fear? Earnestly, though somewhat irrelevantly, she answers that all she has and all she is shall belong to him. Then, with greater fervor, Lohengrin asks his second question, one that has already been answered. If he is victor, he asks, will she have him for her husband? As surely, answers Elsa, as she is now at his feet, will she give him her body and her soul.

That being so, Lohengrin has one demand to make. Very solemnly he tells her she must never ask—or even wonder to herself—whence it is he comes, what his name is, or what sort of man. Almost without seeming to pay attention, Elsa says she will never ask. Lohengrin is not satisfied and in a higher key repeats his solemn demands. The theme to which he sings these words plays a highly dramatic part in the music later on:

No. 8
Lento

Again Elsa promises to abide by all he asks, only this time her reply is much warmer, and Lohengrin is satisfied. He clasps her to his breast with the words, "Elsa, I love you!" and once more the whole assemblage sings its warm and tender expression of awe, this time with greater power, the sopranos carrying the melody. Lohengrin meantime leads Elsa up to the King, who takes her under his protection. He then announces to all that Telramund's charges are false, as God's judgment shall presently prove. Both Saxons and Brabantines are by this time so much impressed with the strange knight that they urge Telramund to give up his case as hopeless.

Telramund, however, is a true knight. Facing Lohengrin directly, he says he would rather die than back down now.

Furthermore, he says, Lohengrin can look just as bold as he likes; he may have come here through some sorcery or other, but justice is on the side of Telramund, as his victory shall shortly prove. When not under the baleful influence of Ortrud, Telramund is an attractive figure; and here the audience cannot help having a liking for him as the underdog.

Under the King's direction, three Saxons and three Brabantines measure out the fighting ground, and the Herald steps into the middle of it to warn the crowd not to interfere. If a freeman interferes, he shall lose a hand; if a serf does it, he shall lose his head. Furthermore, he adds when this is understood, the fighters had better not try any magic or other tricks. Let them trust in God, not in their own strength. The last injunction appeals to both Lohengrin and Telramund, who solemnly repeat it together.

The King then prays to God to give his judgment through the trial by combat, as all uncover (see p. 88). First the five principals (Elsa, Ortrud, Lohengrin, Telramund, and the King) repeat the prayer in moving five-part harmony unaccompanied, and then the chorus joins them in a mighty swell of sound. This prayer, incidentally, is the only passage in the entire opera that is in three-four time. When Elsa has a sufficiently firm and well-placed soprano to dominate the ensemble, its effect is irresistible.

The King returns to his place under the judgment oak, strikes three blows with his sword on his suspended shield as a signal for the trumpeters to sound the royal summons, and the fight is on. The brief battle is, naturally, fought to the Trial by Combat theme (No. 7). Lohengrin is consistently on the offensive, and he shortly fells Telramund with one mighty stroke. Telramund tries to rise but cannot, and Lohengrin proclaims himself victor but spares his opponent's life.

The decision is a decidedly popular one, and the act ends on a long and joyful finale led by Elsa. In the midst of the crowd (and of the many-voiced harmony) the despair of Ortrud and of Telramund is scarcely noticed. In some modern productions, Telramund tries to reach up and get sympathy and help from Ortrud, but she is too much concerned with the failure of her ambitions to pay any attention to her fallen husband—giving us a little extra insight into her unpleasant character.

Just as Telramund drops unconscious at Ortrud's feet, some of the knights lift Lohengrin up on his shield while others carry off Elsa on the King's. That, at least, is what the stage directions say. I have yet to see a Lohengrin and an Elsa who could be comfortably hefted by the gentlemen of the chorus, and so this final jubilatory gesture is usually omitted in performance.

Act Two

DESPITE the brilliant pageantry, despite her own ultimate defeat, it is Ortrud, the outcast, who dominates the second act of *Lohengrin*. Wagner himself described her as "a political woman," a concept that filled him with horror. She is also a sorceress, a devotee of the old gods of evil, and an ambitious, vengeful female. She easily dominates her husband Telramund and Elsa; she comes close to dominating the King and all his followers; and she succeeds in sowing the doubts that eventually bring tragedy.

Before dawn, she is sitting on the steps of the cathedral of Antwerp with her husband, both wearing the dark tatters of outcasts. For a long time neither says a word as the orchestra plays a low, ominous prelude which introduces two new themes of importance. The first denotes evil, always associated with Ortrud:

No. 9
Andante moderato

and the second denotes the temptation and doubt she suggests to Elsa:

No. 10
Andante moderato

The English horn, with its low, nasal tones, enunciates the Warning motive (No. 8), and the lower stringed instruments shudder most of the way through.

Opposite the cathedral steps, which are on the right, are the women's quarters (called the Kemenate in medieval architecture) of the citadel of Antwerp, and in the back are the knights' quarters (called the Pallas). From inside comes some contrasting festal music — brass instruments blowing merrily, followed briefly by Elsa's motive of Innocence (No. 5) played by the higher wood winds.

For those who come to the opera hoping to follow the story by watching the action and lazily listening to the music, the long dialogue between Ortrud and Telramund sounds like so much dull cursing in the dark. What they miss is a remarkable painting of the triumph of evil over a weak good will.

Telramund is the first to break the silence. It is time to go, he says gloomily. They have been banished. Ortrud, darkly mulling over her plots, says she simply cannot leave, and Telramund turns on her, calling her a fiend. She has wrecked his honor, he says, caused his sword and spear to be broken and his name cursed so that even robbers will have nothing to do with him. Almost weeping, he wishes he had died before such things had happened, and overcome with passion, he throws himself on the ground. The festal trumpet calls inside ironically punctuate his despairing cries, but Ortrud remains completely unmoved. "What are you crying about?" she asks scornfully. "Because I have even lost the weapon to kill you with!" he howls.

Then when Ortrud retains her attitude of quiet scorn, he recalls the details of their peculiar courtship—how in her dark castle in the woods she told him that she herself had seen

Elsa drown her little brother in a pool, how she had tempted him with predictions that her own ancient Frisian line would soon again rule in Brabant, and how she had seduced him into renouncing Elsa to marry Ortrud.

This last accusation finally gets through to Ortrud's somewhat obscure femininity. "It was all true," she says. And as for Telramund's ridiculous belief that God gave Lohengrin the victory, that is a conviction based on his own cowardice. If he had just shown as much fight against the stranger as he is now showing against a woman, he would have won. She invites him to sit down next to her while she tells what her prophetic eye sees. Telramund begins to weaken and to listen as she spins her plans.

This stranger, who came here drawn by a swan: who is he? What would Telramund give to know? Especially when she informs him—as she does now—that if he were compelled to tell his name and lineage, all his supernatural strength would vanish? No one, however, can make him reveal that secret but Elsa herself.

Telramund begins to see the drift of things. "So Elsa has to be persuaded to ask the question?" he asks.

"You're getting smart," says Ortrud. "That is why it is so important not to leave now. Rouse suspicion in her. Accuse him of using magic to circumvent the justice of the trial by combat. And should that scheme fail, we still can try force. For according to what I know of black magic, a man who gains his victories through it loses all his power if he sheds just one drop of his blood through the smallest wound. If you had so much as scratched his finger, he would have been in your power."

The idea that he had been tricked into defeat wins over Telramund. Had he but known! And even now, he can get his revenge and win back his honor. For a moment he wonders whether Ortrud may not be lying to him once more; but she needs only to mention the sweetness of revenge to win him over once and for all. Together they sit there on the ground and solemnly swear vengeance on those still sleeping in the castle,

Softly the wood winds give out the theme of Elsa's happi-

No. 11
Lento

ness and she appears, dressed in a white robe, on the balcony of the Kemenate. Leaning her head on her hand, she sings to the breezes that used so often to hear her complaints: now she has only to tell them of her coming happiness and of her great love (see page 92). Ortrud sees her chance. Not trusting her bumbling Telramund, she sends him off so that she herself may make the first move in their great gamble.

She plays it with consummate skill. What harm, she asks, had she ever done Elsa? Was it simply that Telramund had chosen to marry her after Elsa had rejected him? He was a poor, misguided fellow when he accused Elsa, but now he is eating out his heart with remorse. "Oh, you are happy," Ortrud goes on, "after your brief period of blameless sorrows: and now you can send me on the road to death so that my cries will not penetrate your happiness."

Elsa cannot resist this false show of pathos. What an ungrateful wretch she would be, she says, if she repaid her debt of great happiness by spurning the humbled unhappiness that bows before her. "Wait a moment, Ortrud," she calls down. "I shall let you in here myself."

While Elsa descends the steps inside, the singer who does the part of Ortrud has her great moment—that is, if she has a good, reliable high A sharp in her. She drops her mask of humbleness completely, and in a wild frenzy calls on the great gods Wotan and Freia* to assist her now in her planned deceit.

When Elsa arrives downstairs, she is shocked by the condition in which she finds Ortrud, humble and prostrate on the ground. She raises her enemy, asks forgiveness of her for the unhappiness she has caused, and promises, after her marriage, to intercede with Lohengrin on behalf of Telramund. Ortrud, of course, feigns the greatest gratitude and wonders what she can do to repay such generosity. Maybe, she artfully suggests, she can save Elsa future unhappiness. Had Elsa perhaps ever thought that one who came to her through magic might depart the same way? The motives of Warning (No. 8) and of Doubt (No. 10) are used here with great effect. They imply that though Elsa immediately turns away from such suggestions, she is still seized with misgivings. Sorrow and compassion win for the moment, however; and in her innocent fashion she pities Ortrud for not appreciating the rapture of trust and of love. While she delivers her little homily, Ortrud makes a duet of it by saying (aside, of course) that she intends to turn this loving trust into a weapon to bring misfortune to Elsa (see p. 96). Despite Ortrud's ominous mutterings, the duet is made one of the warmest passages of music in the opera by two lovely motives, which, unfortunately, are used nowhere else—the motive of Perfect Faith

No. 12
Moderato

and of Confidence

No. 13
Tranquillo

Elsa finally invites her enemy to come into the Kemenate with her and bedeck herself with fine clothes for the wedding. Ortrud, who is given a little overmuch to melodramatics, here stands aside for Elsa to lead the way and then, after she has gone through the door, delivers one final horrid grimace at the audience.

The first faint gleam of dawn comes on the stage as Telramund, to the motive of Evil (No. 9), comes out from where he has overheard the foregoing scene and says, "Thus evil enters this house." The observation is hardly flattering to his wife, but he rationalizes away his last remaining shreds of honor by saying that the only course left open to him now is to destroy him who brought dishonor.

Day begins to dawn in earnest now as two pairs of trumpets answer each other back and forth from towers near and far. Life stirs in the courtyard as various menials go about drawing water, opening gates, or simply going in and out. The four trumpeters enter from the Pallas to deliver the royal summons (No. 3), and the nobles of the chorus file in from various directions in answer to it, all completely dressed and ready, singing a concerted number to the promise of the new day. It is a good double chorus Wagner has supplied, but often it is

cut. The Herald comes forth with the latest news, given in three sections, each dutifully hailed by the noblemen. First: Telramund has been banished, and anyone who helps him shall suffer the same fate. Second: the God-sent stranger, who has earned the hand of Elsa and with it the crown and lands of Brabant, has no ambitions to be called a duke. Therefore he should hereafter be addressed as Guardian of Brabant.† And third: today the wedding shall be celebrated; tomorrow everyone should bring weapons. For the bridegroom scorns rest and plans to follow the King into battle, where glory is to be earned.

Everyone is vociferously delighted with these pronouncements, and the jubilation begins and ends with the Lohengrin motive (No. 6) crashed out fortissimo. Everyone, that is, but four discontented nobles who appeared briefly in the first act as adherents of Telramund and who now form an isolationist party, his Majesty's disloyal opposition. "Listen to that," they mutter, "he wants to lead us away from home tomorrow against a foe that has not attacked us." Just then Telramund steps into their midst out of his hiding place and offers to accuse Lohengrin of sorcery. The four are frightened by his sudden appearance, and they hustle him off to one side.‡

Four page boys (two sopranos and two altos) clear the way for Elsa, whom they announce; and the prenuptial procession and music begin, the noblewomen filing in to a slow, stately measure, out of the Kemenate, down the stairs, and over toward the cathedral (see p. 100). The music, which has a warm, quiet pomp about it, is based chiefly on the theme of Elsa's Happiness (No. 11) and another known as the motive of Love's Consecration:

No. 14
Lento maestoso

In fine six-part chorus writing, the music mounts to a splendid climax as the procession slowly approaches the cathedral steps. It has just reached this climax, when Ortrud suddenly appears at the top of the steps and comes out in her true colors. She stops everything to demand her rightful place, before Elsa. (The poor bride can scarcely believe this change in the woman she had befriended.) Ortrud dramatically reminds everyone that before Lohengrin came, Telramund was honored before all. But now who can honor Lohengrin when even his bride is not allowed to name him? "Can you name him?" she asks. "Can you tell us whether he is of noble birth, or where he came from—or when and where he is going off again? Of course not. The answers would put him in a bad light. That is why the clever hero forbade your asking!"

Elsa rises to the occasion as best she can. With considerable spirit she answers that anyone can see what a noble and good man her knight is. Besides, with God's help he has defeated Ortrud's husband. Therefore, let the people judge which of the two is the purer man. The crowd acclaims Lohengrin.

---

*These, of course, are the same gods for whom Wagner shows so much respect and sympathy in the Ring. Wotan's taste for deceit and his incompetence in practicing it are evident in the later operas too, but there Wagner seems to be for instead of against him.

†This touch may have been inspired by the extreme leftist political ideas Wagner was entertaining at the time he wrote the libretto.

‡Economical opera companies omit the whole incident of the four knights, which is not necessary to the story.

But this argument is not good enough for Ortrud. She presses home her point that Lohengrin had to use some mysterious magic to gain his victory, and that it is made all the more suspicious by Elsa's refusal to ask his name. If she does not dare do it, everyone must believe that she has serious doubts herself about what sort of man he is.

Ortrud's position is unanswerable, and Elsa is saved just in time by the arrival of the King and Lohengrin, accompanied by the Saxon nobles and, of course, the royal summons on the trumpets. The weeping Elsa puts her head on Lohengrin's breast and begs to be saved from that woman. Lohengrin imperiously orders Ortrud away and then, with Elsa and the King, again starts leading the procession into the cathedral.

Their troubles are not yet over. This time Telramund shows up on the cathedral steps to interrupt the wedding and to accuse Lohengrin of having used witchcraft to circumvent God's trial by combat. He has no easy time of it, for he is at once attacked on all sides. Yet he manages to shake himself free; and, forgetting that Ortrud had told him only Elsa could make Lohengrin speak, himself demands his name and rank. Certainly, he heatedly argues, a man who came drawn by such a magical animal as a wild swan cannot be honorable. If he will tell who he is, Telramund will take the consequences; if not, Lohengrin's honor is gone. All the nobles and even the King are impressed, but Lohengrin merely says that so dishonored a man does not need to be answered. Then, says Telramund, let the King himself intervene and ask the questions.

But before the embarrassed King can even frame a reply, Lohengrin says he would not answer even him if he were to ask—this King or any other mortal king. Only to Elsa must he reply if she asks. Does she?

For a long while, to Lohengrin's horror, she hesitates and says nothing. Then she shilly-shallies. It would be ungrateful, she says, to force the man who saved her to reveal his obviously dangerous secret. Yet, if she knew it, she is sure she could keep it close. And also, she says, some doubt has now arisen in her heart. It is difficult to follow Elsa's vacillating mind here, especially as everyone else is expressing his own feelings at the same time. It all adds up, however, to a splendid ensemble. The King ends it by advising Lohengrin not to reply to Telramund. The knights, too, express their confidence in their new leader, and he thanks them. While the mutual congratulations are going on, Telramund sneaks up to Elsa and whispers that he will be near at hand that night; for if he can but scratch Lohengrin, the secret will be out. Falteringly, Elsa refuses to have anything to do with him; and when Lohengrin sees who is talking to his bride, he orders Telramund away.

Now at last the procession can get on into the cathedral, which it does to an ever-mounting crescendo. As Lohengrin and Elsa reach the top of the stairs, he takes her in his arms.

But over his shoulder she sees Ortrud, once more in the foreground, her arm raised as though in victory—while the trumpets and trombones in the orchestra loudly and ominously blow the Warning motive (No. 8).

Act Three, Prelude

THE Prelude to the third act of *Lohengrin* is deservedly one of the most popular pieces in the concert repertoire (see p. 104). It starts off with tremendous energy in festive mood with fiddles sawing away for dear life and cymbals crashing on off beats. Presently the cellos, bassoons, and French horns snort out a theme of such strength that it takes all the violins playing as loud as they can to keep it in place, only to have the theme repeated with the stentorian reinforcement of trombones. At one point, where the theme in the bass has a short rest (the twenty-fourth bar, if you want to refer to it on p. 105), the violins have a little figure in unison as though trying to gather strength to resist again the onslaught of the heavier instruments. That bar is a serious hurdle for an orchestra that has been under- or incompetently rehearsed. On those occasions, it sounds not only excited but confused.

The Prelude is, of course, suggestive of the wedding celebration; and in the middle there is a tender section scored for the wind instruments which brings to mind again Elsa's purity. Too many conductors here fall into the trap of slowing up in the interests of sentiment and hurting the impact of the piece as a whole.

In the concert arrangement, made by Wagner, the piece ends with a heavy reiteration of the fateful Warning motive (No. 8). In the opera itself, however, the Prelude dies down and modulates quietly into the even more famous "Bridal Chorus" (see p. 113).

Act Three, Scene 1

THE "Bridal Chorus" is, of course, the "Wedding March from *Lohengrin*" used at weddings all over the Western world, with the bride marching down the aisle on the arm of her father. There is this difference: the tempo taken in church is much slower than the one in the opera. The stage shows Elsa and Lohengrin's bridal chamber, a couch and a window in a recess on the right side. The music comes from off stage at first; then torch-bearing pages enter, followed by ladies in waiting conducting Elsa in from the door on the left, while King Henry and the men escort Lohengrin in from the right. The two processions meet; Elsa and Lohengrin, left in the center, are relieved of their outer garments by pages; eight women walk

around the couple twice, singing their best wishes for a happy marriage; and then the two groups file out through the doors opposite those from which they entered.*

The duet that follows is a remarkable piece of musicodramatic craftsmanship and inspiration, for it combines the most tender love melodies with the clear tracing of Elsa's upsurging curiosity about Lohengrin's name, and his growing dismay as his efforts to avoid the fatal questions fail one after the other.

With the last faint echo of the "Bridal Chorus," Lohengrin takes Elsa into his arms—the first time, as he says, that they have been alone since they have met. Is she happy to be his bride? "Happy" is too cold a word for one who now knows all the joy of heaven, responds Elsa, and she sings a love melody to him of deep warmth and restraint.

No. 15
Molto tranquillo

Love such as this en-flames my in-most be - ing,
Fühl ich zu dir so süss mein Herz ent-bren-nen,
Gods on - ly know the rap-ture that I feel.
ath - me ich Won - nen, die nur Gott ver-leiht.

Lohengrin takes it up too, and finally their voices blend in soft rapture (see p. 117).

It is the last pure moment of joy they have. Lohengrin—in the way lovers have of recalling their earliest moments together —sings of how he had come though he did not even know who she was: her look was enough to make him feel her innocence.

*The marching on and off presents an interesting little problem in choral singing. It is difficult for a chorus to keep its rhythm and pitch if it starts singing off stage under an assistant conductor, has to march on under none, pick up its cue from the conductor in the pit, and then march off again. At the Metropolitan this problem is neatly solved by having an off-stage chorus sing till the procession is on stage. The singers on stage take up at the point where they are all standing still, and as soon as they start off again, the off-stage chorus takes up. Unless you watch their mouths closely, the little deception remains unnoticed. Companies with smaller choruses that cannot be divided usually find the final echolike phrase sung unaccompanied off stage almost half a tone flat.

Elsa recalls how she had first seen him in a dream, and how deeply she felt even then. "Is this love and nothing more?" she asks. "How can I name it—any more than I can name your own name?" And when unsuspecting Lohengrin caressingly pronounces hers, she asks whether he cannot tell her his name in the privacy of their love so that she may pronounce it as he has hers. No one else in the world shall hear it.

Lohengrin leads her to the window, points out to the flower garden, and tells her—again in a warmly rapturous melody— that her innocence had pervaded his soul and made him love her long before he knew of her rank, just as the odor of the flowers pervades everything here (see p. 120). Elsa cannot take the hint. If only, she says, she could help him somehow; perhaps some danger is lurking in his secret. If she could share that danger, no power on earth could wrest the secret from her. "Let me but know who you are," she goes on, despite Lohengrin's pleas for her to stop; "entrust me with the secret of the place you came from, and you shall see how well I can guard the knowledge."

Elsa has now practically broken her promise never to ask the questions, and for a few brief phrases Lohengrin addresses her sternly. He has shown her the greatest trust in believing her vow; let her, above all women, give him an equal trust. Then tenderness once more comes over him. He loves her so much, he says, that he would gladly lay down crowns for her. Indeed, he comes from a country that is bright with joy.

What he had intended to be reassurance only makes Elsa more curious and more unhappy. If he has come from so happy a place, she reasons, how long can she expect him to stay here? Soon she must lose him. Magic brought him here; magic will take him away again. How can she prevent it? She becomes wilder and more unstable—and suddenly she imagines she sees the swan coming to take Lohengrin away. All of Lohengrin's frantic imploring does no good now. With the music mounting in excitement, she pronounces the fatal questions in precisely the words that had been forbidden her.

At that very moment, she sees Telramund and his four followers sneaking into the room with drawn swords. With a shriek, she warns Lohengrin and hands him his sword. He turns on Telramund, kills him with one magical blow; and as the terrified followers sink to their knees, Elsa faints away. There is a long silence broken only by very soft, nervous beats on the kettledrum—and the cellos breathe out the motive of Evil (No. 9).

"Ah, woe! Now all our luck is gone!" moans Lohengrin.

He gently places Elsa on the couch as a clarinet stops halfway through the melody of love Elsa had sung early in the scene (No. 15). Then he directs the four men to bring the body of Telramund to the King's judgment seat, strikes a bell to summon two women in waiting, and instructs them to dress Elsa for an appearance before the King, where she shall finally learn the answer to her questions. Once more the Warning motive (No. 8) is heard, and the curtain falls.

Act Three, Scene 2

WHILE the scenery is changed* the orchestral strings make a rumbling hurly-burly, and brassy military calls sound off and on the stage to denote the gathering of the clans before the judgment oak, as in Act I. The rising curtain reveals this gathering, and presently the King comes on to address the Brabantines and thank them for their loyalty. He is just asking for Lohengrin, when the four nobles bring in the body of Telramund on a bier covered with a blanket. They say that the Guardian of Brabant has ordered this brought forth and that he will explain it all shortly. Then Elsa comes on with her ladies in waiting, so pale and weak that the King asks what the trouble can be. Is she so much moved by the prospect of being parted from her bridegroom? Elsa is incapable of answering. The orchestra does it for her sadly by blowing her theme of Innocence (No. 5b)—but, for the first time, in a minor key.

Lohengrin comes on armed as in Act I and is joyfully greeted by both King and nobles, who are eager for him to lead them into battle. That cannot be, he says; it is forbidden.

He comes now not as a warrior, but as a complainant—and he dramatically uncovers the corpse of Telramund.†

"First," he asks, "was I not right to kill this man, who attacked me last night?" They all agree.

And now for his other complaint. Everyone has heard Elsa's promise that she would never ask who he was. She has succumbed to bad advice and broken her oath, and therefore he must give the answers before them all. Let them hear now whether he is not the equal of anyone present.

Accompanied by the theme of the Holy Grail, and using much of the music which Wagner further intensified when he came to composing the Prelude to the opera, Lohengrin sings his "Narrative" (see p. 126). He tells about the castle of Monsalvat, where the Grail is guarded by a band of holy knights. Each year a dove descends from heaven to strengthen the mystic powers of the Grail. Those who guard it receive magical powers; those who evilly oppose these guardians lose all their

---

*This change is quickly effected because the first scene uses only the front of the stage.

†Out of respect for the star baritone who sings Telramund, he is not usually asked to lend his body to these proceedings. The effect of Lohengrin's gesture is consequently weakened when he lifts only one corner of the blanket, giving the King a peek but none to the audience.

own power. No matter to what distant lands the knights errant are sent on their deeds of goodness, the power remains undiminished so long as the knights remain unknown. Once, however, they are recognized, they must return. The Grail has sent him here: he is the son of the reigning King Parsifal, and he is called Lohengrin.

A full orchestral statement of the Lohengrin theme (No. 6) follows this final announcement, and immediately afterwards the King and the chorus, singing in six parts, express their sorrow to the melody of the beautiful descending theme of Farewell (No. 2). As Elsa is about to faint, Lohengrin catches her in his arms and sorrowfully chides her for what she has done to him. Elsa cannot accept—can scarcely comprehend—the tragedy that has overtaken her. She begs for any punishment, just so that her husband may remain with her. In a long concerted number she continues to plead, while Lohengrin says it is impossible to stay, and the chorus and King alternately seem to understand that his leaving is mandatory, and beg him nevertheless to remain with them. Finally Lohengrin has to tell them that if he did stay, all his prowess as a warrior would fail him. Yet, he adds, the King should know that a great victory is in store for him and that never again shall "the Eastern hordes" be victorious.

At that moment the men at the bank of the river see the swan coming once more, and everyone shouts in excitement. Elsa starts up in horror: the vision she had seen while in Lohengrin's arms has materialized. To the Swan theme (No. 1a), Lohengrin begins his last farewell. He greets the swan with a sad affection; then in an outburst of deep pain he comes

back to Elsa and tells her that had he but been able to stay with her for one year, the Grail would have sent her brother back to her. Should he come home after Lohengrin is far away, Elsa is to give him Lohengrin's horn, his sword, and his ring. He gives these tokens to her and then, kissing the almost insensible girl repeatedly, he sings his last heartbroken *Leb' wohl* and rushes up to the bank of the river (see p. 132). Only Ortrud remains unshaken. In a burst of triumphant fiendishness, she urges the proud knight to sail home while she tells Elsa a fine tale. For by a little chain about the swan's neck she recognizes the animal as the rightful heir of Brabant, whom she had changed into a swan. "The vengeance of the gods is on you!" she shouts.

Lohengrin hears her from the bank, sinks down on his knees; and a miracle occurs as the orchestra betrays its source with the theme of the Holy Grail (No. 1). From the clouds there slowly descends the white dove of whom Lohengrin had spoken in his narrative and takes up the boat's chain. The swan sinks into the water, and in his place young Godfrey springs ashore. "Behold the Duke of Brabant, who should be named your leader!" cries Lohengrin. He then steps into the boat and is slowly drawn down the river while the orchestra plays the heroic Lohengrin theme (No. 6).

For a moment Elsa takes Godfrey in her arms, then runs to the shore to call frantically after her husband. He, however, slowly disappears, his head bowed, and leaning on his shield. The orchestra plays his theme once more, this time in minor. Ortrud gives a despairing cry as she recognizes Godfrey, and Elsa sinks lifeless into his arms.

Prelude

Original key

Adagio

Elsa's Dream

EINSAM IN TRÜBEN TAGEN

Original key: A-flat

Friend - less and all for - sak - en, Bur - dened with grief and
Ein - sam in trü - ben Ta - gen hab' ich zu Gott ge -

care, By sor - row o - ver - tak - en, I turned to God in
fleht, des Her - zens tief - stes Kla - gen er - goss' ich im Ge -

prayer. When all the world was sleep - ing, My cries a - woke the
bet: da drang aus mei - nem Stöh - nen ein Laut so kla - ge -

night, Fill - ing the air with sigh - ing, Mount - ing to
voll, der zu ge - walt' - gem Tö - nen weit in die

heav - en's height! And soon I ceased from
Lüf - te schwoll: Ich hört' ihn fern hin

sigh - ing, My eyes for - got to weep; And then on God re-
hal - len, bis kaum mein Ohr er traf; mein Aug' ist zu - ge-

ly - ing, At last I fell a - sleep.
fal - len, ich sank in sü - ssen Schlaf.

THE KING

El - sa,   de - fend your-self be - fore   the court!
El - sa,   ver - theid' - ge dich vor dem   Ge - richt!

poco cresc.   *dim.*   *pp*

p   *più p*

ELSA *pp*

A   vis - ion fills   my   dream - ing,   A   knight   in full   ar -
In   lich - ter Waf - fen   Schei - ne   ein   Rit - ter nah - te

pp

(animating the time a little)

ray;   I   saw his ar - mor gleam - ing,   His
da,   so   tu - gend - li - cher Rei - ne ich

p 6

face was like the day! His gold-en horn___ was sound-ing, He
kei - nen noch er-sah, *ein gol-den Horn___ zur Hüf-ten,* *ge-*

bore___ a knight-ly sword; Ah, so when he looked up-
leh - net auf sein Schwert, *so* *trat er aus den*

on me, My faith was all re-stored. His
Lüf-ten *zu mir, der Re - - cke werth;* *mit*

bright - ness seemed to warm me Like___
züch - ti - gem Ge-bah - - ren *gab___*

sempre p

p

) 82 (

firmly

heav - en's glow - ing flame; My____
Trö - stung er mir ein; *des____*

knight in shin - ing ar - mor, He____
Rit - ters will ich wah - ren, er____

____ shall de - fend my name! He who is
____ soll mein Strei - ter sein! Hört, was dem

sent to me to re - store____ my fair re - nown, shall
Gott ge - sand - ten ich bie - te für Ge - währ: in

) 83 (

rule my fa - ther's vas - sals. And wear _____ my fa-ther's
mei - nes Va - ters Lan - den, die Kro - ne tra - ge

crown; If he will dare be - friend me And
er; mich glück - lich soll ich prei - sen, And nimmt

take me for his wife, If he will dare de -
er mein Gut da - hin, will er Ge - mahl mich

fend me, I'll pledge him love and life!
hei - ssen, geb' ich ihm, was ich bin!

Your Task Is Done

NUN SEI BEDANKT

Adagio   LOHENGRIN   Original key: A

Your task is done, my
Nun sei be-dankt, mein

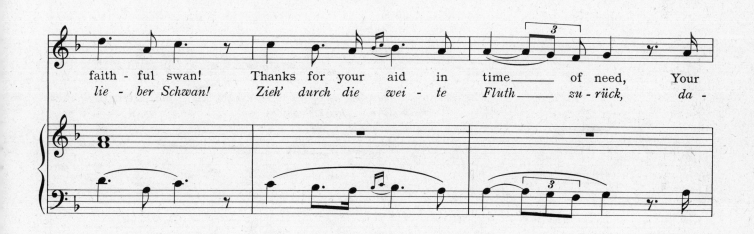

faith - ful swan! Thanks for your aid in time___ of need, Your
lie - ber Schwan! Zieh' durch die wei - te Fluth___ zu - rück, da -

help in this my chos - en quest. Sail home a - gain with
hin, wo - her mich trug dein Kahn, kehr' wie - der nur zu

joy - ful speed, Home to that land so tru - ly blest.
un - serm Glück! Drum sei ge - treu dein Dienst___ ge - than!

Sail on! Sail on! my faith - ful swan!
Leb' wohl! Leb' wohl! mein lie - ber Schwan!

CHORUS

Here is a knight___ of strength and
Wie fasst uns se - lig sü - sses

splen - dor, a___ mar - vel no man may___ with - stand. Here is her
Grau - en, welch'___ hol - de Macht hält uns___ ge - bannt! Wie ist er

) 86 (

knight, her true_____ de - fend - er, Shed - ding a glo - ry in our
schön und hehr_____ zu schau - en, den solch' ein Wun - der trug an's

land! Here is a knight_ of beau - ty and splen - dor who_ sheds_____ a
Land! Wie ist er schön_ und_ hehr_____ zu schau - en, den_ solch'_____ ein

glo - ry in our_ land!
Wun - der trug an's_ Land!

The King's Prayer

MEIN HERR UND GOTT

Original key

Solemnly — THE KING

Oh Lord and God, be with us now! Give us thy judg - ment clear and strong, Be - fore thy word all men shall bow that
Mein Herr und Gott, nun ruf' ich dich, das du dem Kampf zu - ge - gen sei'st! Durch Schwer - tes Sieg ein Ur - theil sprich, das

right may___ tri - umph o - - ver wrong.
Trug und___ Wahr - heit klar___ er - weist!

KING and CHORUS

Give strength to him whose
Des Rei - - nen Arm gieb___

heart is true, And give the
Hel - den - kraft, des Fal - schen

guilt - y one his due;_____
Stär - ke sei er - schlafft,_____

thou,   oh   God   de - fend,   the
Herr   und   Gott,   nun zög' - re

poco cresc.   *mf*

right!   Oh   Lord
nicht!   Du   Herr,

poco cresc.

cresc.   *f*

our   God,   de
mein   Gott,   nun

cresc.   *f*   *più f*

fend   the   right.
zög' - re   nicht.

ff

Oh Wind That Heard My Weeping

EUCH LÜFTEN, DIE MEIN KLAGEN

Andante

Original key

ELSA

Oh wind that heard my weep - ing, and waft - ed it a -
Euch Lüf - ten, die mein Kla - gen so trau - rig oft er -

bove,_____ Take in your ten - der keep - ing my new - found joy and
füllt,_____ euch muss ich dan - kend sa - gen, wie sich mein Glück ent -

ORTRUD FREDERICK ELSA

love. It's El-sa! El-sa! With you help-ing to lead him,
hüllt. Sie ist es! El-sa! Durch euch kam er ge - zo - gen,

) 92 (

oh, light-ly laugh-ing breeze, He found a wind to
ihr lä - chel - tet der Fahrt, auf wil - den Mee - res -

speed him through wild and storm - y seas.
wo - gen habt ihr ihn treu be - wahrt.

ORTRUD

She'll rue the e - vil
Der Stun - de soll sie

In times of grief and sad - ness you
Zu trock - nen mei - ne Zäh - ren hab'

mo - ment when she dared to cross my path!
flu - chen, in der sie jetzt mein Blick ge - wahrt!

dried my tears a - way! Come now in love's sweet
ich euch oft ge - müht; wollt Küh - lung nun ge -

mad - ness and cool its burn - ing ray.
wäh - ren der Wang', in Lieb' er - glüht!

FREDERICK
Why not?
Wa - rum?

ORTRUD (to Frederick)
Be off! Your be - ing here would nev-er do!
Hin-weg! Ent-fern' ein Klei-nes dich von hier!

ELSA
Oh cool
Wollt Küh -

(Frederick slinks away)

I'll see to her, her champ - ion is for you!
Sie ist für mich, ihr Held ge - hö - re dir!

this burn-ing mad-ness   of   love!
-lung nun ge-wäh-ren   der Wang',

mf   p

Of____ glad - ness,   this mad - ness   of   joy   and
in____ Lie - be,   in   Lie - be,   in   Lieb'   er -

mf   p   pp   più p

love.   This glad - - ness!
glüht!   In   Lie - - be!

pp

pp

Ped.   ✻

No Words of Mine

DU ÄRMSTE

Original key: G

No words of mine can ev - er meas - ure what joy a trust - ing heart __ may own, Have you not known the sa - cred pleas - ure, the soul may find in faith a - lone?

Du Ärm - ste kannst wohl nie er - mes - sen, wie zwei - fel - los mein Her - ze liebt! Du hast wohl nie das Glück __ be - ses - sen, das sich uns nur durch Glau - be giebt!

Stay here a - while, Let me per - suade you what
Kehr' bei mir ein! Lass' mich dich leh - ren, wie

ho - ly rap - ture faith may be - stow, Faith in the
süss die Won - ne rein - ster Treu'! Lass' zu dem

lov - ing pow'r that made you, The
Glau - ben dich be - keh - ren: es

bright - est joy, the high - est joy, the heart may
giebt ein Glück, es giebt ein Glück, das oh - ne

Bridal Procession

Largo e solenne

Prelude to Act 3 and Bridal Chorus

Original key

love ev - er sound! Bold - est of he - roes
se - lig - sten Paar. Strei - ter der Tu - gend

lead in your bride! Fair - est of maid - ens
schrei - te vor - an! Zier - de der Ju - gend,

stay by his side! Now that the sounds of
schrei - te vor - an! Rau - schen - des Fes - tes

mirth have a - bat - ed, This is the hour so
seid nun ent - ron - nen, Won - ne des Her - zens

fond - ly a - wait - ed,   Here   in this   home   of
sei euch ge - won - nen!   *Duf - ten - der Raum,*   *zur*

love's__ true de - light   May they ful - fill the
Lie - be ge - schmückt,   *Nehm' euch nun auf, dem*

joys of__ this__ night.__   Long may you live,
Glan - ze__ ent - rückt.__   *Treu - lich ge - führt*

Long may you love,   Long may the bless - ings of
zie - het nun ein,   *Wo euch der Se - gen der*

heav - en a - bound.
Lie - be be - wahr'!
Come val - iant knight,
Sieg - rei - cher Muth,

Come love - ly maid,
Min - ne so rein
Here may the mu - sic of
eint euch in Treu - e zum

love_____
se - - - - - lig - sten Paar,
ev - er sound,

The mu - sic of love!_____
zum se - lig - sten Paar!_____

) 116 (

How Can I Tell

FÜHL' ICH ZU DIR

Molto tranquillo

Original key: E

How can I tell the joy my heart is feel - ing?
Fühl' ich zu dir so süss mein Herz ent - bren - nen,

Love is a bless - ing sent from God a - bove; How to ex - press what
ath - me ich Won - nen, die nur Gott ver - leiht, fühl' ich zu dir so

heav'n is re - veal - ing? Love is a bless-ing sent from God____ a - bove! Be -
süss mich ent - bren nen, ath - me ich Won - nen, die nur Gott____ ver - leiht. Ver -

LOHENGRIN

hold my heart be - fore your beau - ty kneel - ing
magst du, Hol - de, glück - lich dich zu nen - nen,

Pray - ing to gain the heav - en of your love.
giebst du auch mir des Him - mels Se - lig - keit!

(tenderly)
How can I tell the joy my heart is feel - ing,
Fühl' ich zu dir so süss mein Herz ent - bren - nen,

Love is a bless - ing sent from God a - bove.
ath - me ich Won - nen, die nur Gott ver - leiht;

Ah, How the Flowers

ATHMEST DU NICHT

Original key: C

seen _____ a blos - som half so
erst, _____ du Sü - sse, dich er -

sweet. No need to
sah; nicht dei - ne

ask _____ how God had made such
Art _____ ich brauch - te zu er -

beau - ty, There was your face! My
kun - den, dich sah mein Aug'; mein

heart was at your feet.
Herz be - griff dich da.

Just as the
Wie mir die

flow'rs have wrapt their spell a -
Düf - te hold den Sinn be -

round me,
rü - cken,

Though all was
nah'n sie mir

dark, though cold the mid - night
gleich aus räth - sel-vol - ler

Lohengrin's Narrative

IN FERNEM LAND

Far, far a-way,   be-
In fer - nem Land,   un-

yond the ken of mor - tals,   There stands the tow'r   of   Mon - sal - vat, the blest.
nah - bar eu - ren Schrit - ten,   liegt ei - ne Burg, die Mon - sal - vat ge - nannt;

It holds a shrine guard-ed by. gold-en por-tals,   more   sa - cred and re-vered than all   the
ein lich - ter Tem - pel ste-het dort in - mit-ten,   so   kost - bar, als auf Er - den nichts be-

rest. There is a cup up-on that bless-ed al-tar Of beau-ty nev-er
kannt; drin ein Ge-fäss von wun-der-thät'-gem Se-gen wird dort als höch-stes

seen by sin-ful eyes. For those who take the vow and nev-er fal-ter, The
Hei-lig-thum be-wacht; es ward, dass sein der Men-schen rein-ste pfle-gen, her-

cup was brought by an-gels from the skies. And once a year, a
ab von ei-ner En-gel-schaar ge-bracht; all-jähr-lich naht vom

dove comes down from heav-en, To strength-en and re-fresh its ho-ly
Him-mel ei-ne Tau-be, um neu zu stär-ken sei-ne Wun-der-

spell, It's called the Grail!_ Its sa-cred pow'r is giv-en To guard each
kraft: es heisst der Gral,_ und se- lig rein- ster Glau - be er-theilt durch

knight from all the pow'rs of hell. And when the Grail has called a knight to
ihn sich sei - ner Rit - ter - schaft. Wer nun dem Gral zu die - nen ist er -

serve it, His arm is strong with more than mor - tal pow'r. For
ko - ren, den rü - stet er mit ü - ber - ir - di-scher Macht; an

val - iant knights who right- ly may _ de - serve it, The
dem _ ist je - des Bö - sen Trug _ ver - lo - ren, wenn

light___ of the Grail___ shines through the dark - est hour.
ihn___ er er - sieht___ weicht dem des To - des Nacht.

He whom the Grail had sent to dis - tant re - gions, To
Selbst wer von ihm in fer - ne Land' ent - sen - det, zum

make___ the cause of truth and right his own, Has the strength to con -
Strei - ter für der Tu - gend Recht er - nannt, dem wird nicht sei - ne

found the temp - ter's le - gions On - ly so long as he re - mains un -
heil' - ge Kraft ent - wen - det, bleibt als sein Rit - ter dort er un - er -

known.
kannt.
The knight who knows the Grail in all its beau - ty, must
So heh - rer Art doch ist des Gra - les Se - gen, ent-

keep all of its se - crets in his heart.
hüllt, muss er des Lai - en Au - ge flieh'n:
To guard his
des Rit - ters

name be - comes his sa - cred du - ty,
drum sollt Zwei - fel ihr nicht he - gen,
if that be
er - kennt ihr

known, He must at once de - part.
ihn, dann muss er von euch zieh'n.
And now, here is the
Nun hört, wie ich ver-

end of this my sto - ry:
bot' - ner Fra - ge loh - ne!

The Grail sent me to
Vom Gral ward ich zu

fight for truth and right;
euch da - her ge - sandt;

My fa - ther, Par - si - fal
mein Va - ter Par - zi - val

reigns there in glo - ry;
trägt sei - ne Kro - ne,

And I, my lords, am Lo - hen-grin, his
sein Rit - ter ich bin Lo - hen-grin ge -

knight.
nannt.

Lohengrin's Farewell

Original key: A

Andante moderato

My faith - ful Swan! Ah, what a sad and woe - ful day, Our
Mein lie - ber Schwan! Ach, die - se letz - te traur' - ge Fahrt, wie

bright-est hopes are dashed_ a-way! One hap-py year soon would have passed, the
gern hätt' ich sie dir___ er-spart! In ei - nem Jahr, wenn dei - ne Zeit im

year your bond - age was ___ to last, Here would you stand, re -
Dienst zu En - de soll - te geh'n, dann, durch des Gra - les

stored and ___ free, Saved by the Ho - ly Grail's de - cree!
Macht be - freit, wollt' ich dich an - ders wie - der seh'n!

Vivo

p molto cresc.

Oh El - sa! Just a year ___ to love each-
_Oh El - sa! Nur ein Jahr ___ an dei - ner_

oth - er, One year be - side me as my faith - ful bride! ___
Sei - te hätt' ich als Zeu - ge dei - nes Glücks er sehnt! ___

Slower

Then would the Grail ___ have re - stored your broth - er, Your lov - ing
Dann kehr - te, se - lig in des Gral's Ge - lei - te, dein Bru - der

Andante moderato

broth-er, who you thought had died.
wie - der, den du todt ge - wähnt.

Triplet figures should be played very softly

If he comes home, when I am far a-way,_____ This
Kommt er dann heim, wenn ich ihm fern im Le - ben, dies

horn, this sword, this ring give him for me._____ The
Horn, dies Schwert, den Ring sollst du ihm ge - ben; dies

sum - mons of the horn brings help in the fray_____ And
Horn soll in Ge-fahr ihm Hül - fe schen-ken, in

from this sword his fierc - est foe shall flee.
wil - - dem Kampf dies Schwert ihm Sieg ver-leiht.

Give him this ring to be a sweet re-
doch bei dem Rin - ge soll er mein ge-

mind - er of one who came to
den - ken, der einst auch dich aus

free you from dis - grace; Long may he live and may the
Schmach und Noth be - freit; ja, bei dem Rin - ge soll er

fates be kind - er when he shall come to
mein ge - den - ken, der einst auch dich aus

take his right-ful place! Fare-well, fare-well, fare-
Schmach und Noth be-freit! *Leb' wohl!* *Leb' wohl!* *Leb'*

well,_____ be-lov-ed one! Fare - well!
*wohl!*_____ *mein sü-sses Weib!* *Leb' wohl!*

Home to the Grail_____ I must be gone!
Mir zürnt der Gral,_____ wenn ich noch bleib'!

Fare - well!_____ Fare - well!_____
*Leb' wohl!*_____ *Leb' wohl!*_____

LA TRAVIATA

Opera in Three Acts

LIBRETTO BY FRANCESCO MARIA PIAVE

MUSIC BY

Giuseppi Verdi

VIOLETTA VALERY	*Soprano*
ALFREDO GERMONT	*Tenor*
GIORGIO GERMONT	*Baritone*
FLORA BERVOIX	*Mezzo-soprano*
GASTONE	*Tenor*
BARON DOUPHOL	*Baritone*
MARQUIS D'OBIGNY	*Bass*
DOCTOR GRENVIL	*Bass*
ANNINA	*Soprano*
GIUSEPPI (Violetta's servant)	*Tenor*

GUESTS OF VIOLETTA AND FLORA, SERVANTS,
DANCERS, OFF-STAGE CHORUS OF REVELERS

TIME: Late 1840's   PLACE: In and near Paris

FIRST PERFORMED AT
Venice, March 6, 1853

La Traviata

GIUSEPPE VERDI

IT IS a little difficult today to appreciate the scandal associated with the story of Verdi's *La Traviata* in the middle of the nineteenth century. The tale of the lovely lady of easy virtue who wins our sympathy by renouncing her one real love and then dying of consumption is sweetly redolent of lavender and old lace. Yet, on moral grounds Victoria's London refused a license for the performance of Dumas's play on which it is based, and permitted a production of the opera only because it was sung in Italian. It was safe to assume the use of a foreign language would protect London's timid morality. Even so, press and pulpit stormed against the "foul and hideous horrors of the book." They were as genuinely shocked as we would be today if, let us say, the stage were to present with tender solicitude the affectionate home life of a white-slaver.

We would be shocked all the more if we were told that the central figure in the drama was sketched from life. That is what Alexandre Dumas *fils* tells us in the preface to his play, *La Dame aux Camélias.** He knew this famous courtesan of the 1840's himself, he tells us, and perhaps he loved her wisely but not too well. She was a farm girl called Alphonsine Plessis, a name she changed to Marie Duplessis for professional reasons when she came to Paris. "She was tall, very slender, black-haired, and with a pink-and-white complexion," wrote Dumas. "She had a small head, long enamel-like eyes, like those of a Japanese, but lively and delicate. Her lips were as red as cherries, and she had the most beautiful teeth in the world. One might call her a Dresden-china miniature. . . . She was one of the last —and one of the few—courtesans who had a heart. Doubtless that is why she died so young. She lacked neither intelligence nor integrity. . . . She had a native distinction, she dressed with taste, and she walked gracefully—almost with nobility."†

Marie's own story, Dumas tells us, did not entirely parallel that of his *Dame aux Camélias*. She did love a gallant young man who, for reasons of his own, refused to live with her. And so her biography stops at the end of the first act of the opera—and it resumes partially in the last. For in 1847 Marie Duplessis did die of consumption, poverty-stricken, at the age of twenty-three. Her career Dumas likened to Penelope's weaving and unweaving her web—"only, it was in the day that Marie destroyed what she had begun at night."

Dumas's novel was published in 1848. His play—the first he ever produced—was put on in Paris in 1852. Verdi saw it there and was deeply impressed. A few months later he had a copy sent to him in Italy and instructed Francesco Piave, who had already supplied him with eight librettos, to get to work on it. Piave made the necessary condensations with greater skill than usual and presented his friend and patron with the most coherent and moving of all the books he wrote for him. Verdi composed the music at white heat but with consummate care. Though he was still putting the finishing touches on *Il Trovatore*, he completed the score of *La Traviata* in four weeks.

Il Trovatore was mounted in Rome on January 19, 1853; *La Traviata*, in Venice on March 6 of the same year. The former was an instant success, the latter an instant failure. The reason for the failure Verdi hinted at in a little letter to Emanuele Muzio: "*Traviata* last night—a fiasco. Was it my fault or the singers'? . . . Time will tell."

It was at least partially the singers' fault. The tenor was hoarse, contemporary accounts tell us, the baritone did not take his role seriously, and the soprano was, as

---

*Dumas defended the single "l" in *Camélias* with a gallantry worthy of the subject. "If I stick to this spelling in spite of objections from the learned, that is because Madame Sand writes it the way I do. I would rather write badly with her than write well with others." Verdi avoided the difficulty when he called his opera *La Traviata*, which means "the woman who strayed"—a more moral title, certainly, but also less fragrant.

†Among the score or so of leading ladies I have seen undertake the part during the past twenty years, only Jarmila Novotna has created any such illusion. Lucrezia Bori came near it (though she was a little small), and Greta Garbo was convincing on the screen—but then, she did not have to sing.

Henry Krehbiel put it, "a lady of mature years and more than generous integumental upholstery." When the fat prima donna pretended to die of consumption in the last act, the audience shrieked with laughter.

Possibly an even greater contributor to the failure was the costuming. It was given in the clothes of the period, and no opera ever appealed to Europeans if the singers were dressed like the audience. A year later *La Traviata* was a success with a different cast and costumes of approximately a century earlier. Today, of course, it is played in costumes of the period of the story—about 1840—though half a century ago, when producers were less conscientious about such details, the leading tenor often wore modern evening clothes in American and English productions while Violetta appeared in the latest *fin de siècle* modes.

Since its *première* the opera has been a great favorite everywhere. In 1856 it was mounted in London, St. Petersburg, New York, and Paris, and though critics found fault with it, the public did not. Its popularity has never waned since. At the Metropolitan Opera House in New York City it is well on its way to its two-hundredth performance, second only to *Aïda* in the Verdi repertoire. The secret of its hold on the public, I am convinced, does not lie merely in the exquisitely pathetic music. The book is sound drama and sound psychology. The reasoning and prejudices of the characters do not on the surface appeal to all modern minds and hearts, but Violetta's emotions are utterly clear and convincing. A woman who stands alone, holding fast to her emotional convictions against the pressures of love and of public opinion, has always had a deep hold on audiences ever since Euripides wrote the *Medea*. Violetta is no Medea, but she is one of the most appealing and heart-rending dramatic figures ever created; and Verdi's apparently simple score is full of subtle touches of psychological insight that the listener unconsciously responds to.

Note-tired critics discover this fact anew when they hear a fine and unfamiliar interpretation. Krehbiel discovered it in 1906, when Sembrich sang Violetta; Olin Downes in 1939, when Novotna first did the role here; Virgil Thomson in 1942, when Licia Albanese was the unhappy heroine. Ordinary listeners, however, make the discovery every time the opera is put on with any pretense to competence.

Prelude

PERHAPS because it is at once so simple and beautiful, no one has ever remarked that the brief Prelude to Act I gives us a summary of the principal cues to the heroine's action and character (see p. 149). The opening theme (with its divided violins that remind some listeners of the Prelude to *Lohengrin*, though the device is older than either *Lohengrin* or *Traviata*) is the soft, sad theme used in the last act to accompany Violetta's illness.

No. 1
Adagio

Then comes a broad, generous melody used with great effect during the second act to express the depth of her sorrow and devotion.

No. 2
Adagio

This is repeated in the cellos a moment later, accompanied in the violins by a light, flirtatious obbligato, suggestive of the love she knew with other men before meeting her Alfredo. The light theme appears to triumph, but twice before the end it is interrupted by the strong love theme—and the Prelude ends quietly, with the staccato sixteenths fading away, as Violetta's own carefree philosophy of life fades away before a strong love at the end of Act I.

Act One

WITH some feverish excitement in the orchestra, the curtain rises to show the salon of Violetta Valery (Marguerite Gautier in Dumas's play), as she is greeting her tardy guests at an evening party. Violetta apparently has the means to entertain a not inconsiderable proportion of the Paris of 1840 that can afford both evening clothes and being seen at the home of a lovely lady of doubtful reputation. Her more intimate friends—those who sit with her at the central table, while the others (members of the chorus) fill up the rest—include her friend Flora Bervoix, her physician Dr. Grenvil, a prominent candidate for her favors named Baron Douphol, the Marquis d'Obigny, and Gastone, Vicomte de Letorières. Because the opera is always sung here either in Italian or in a substitute for literate English that might as well be a foreign language, we usually miss the significance of the masterly and highly compressed opening exposition. Against a gay and shallow staccato tune in the orchestra,

No. 3
Allegro vivace

we learn that it is already late for the party to start, that Flora delayed the rest of the guests, that her intimate friends wonder whether Violetta really is well enough to be giving this party, and that she has thrown caution to the winds, risking her health to have a good time.

To a smoother but still restless melody,

No. 4
Allegro

the Viscount now introduces a young friend from the country,

Alfredo Germont. The guests are seated under Violetta's general direction, and at his first opportunity Gastone tells Violetta of the young man's devotion. Each morning during her recent illness he stayed near her house, even though he had never met her. Meantime Baron Douphol finds an opportunity to tell Flora he does not particularly like this upstart; and when he is asked to sing a song, the Baron (a surly fellow throughout the opera) refuses and suggests Alfredo instead. On Violetta's special request, the young man consents, and while he clinks glasses all around, the orchestra strikes up the Drinking Song ("*Libiamo*"—"Let's drink"), stopping the introduction in mid-career, while the leading tenor climbs aboard. He sings, of course, in praise of wine, wit, and beauty, with a special bow to Violetta (see p. 152). She takes up the strain with even more impassioned words, a paraphrase of Herrick's "Gather ye rose-buds while ye may, Old Time is still a-flying." It sums up her present philosophy of life admirably. The chorus then sings it too, and before it is over we have Alfredo and Violetta answering each other, phrase by phrase, the young man expressing his love with little disguise under cover of the song. They join in the refrain, while the chorus supplies a restless staccato background.

Now the dance band Violetta has engaged for the evening starts playing. (Verdi wanted a stage band for the purpose, but in modern performances he seldom gets it.) Violetta's invitation to go into the next room and dance is joyfully accepted by her guests; but as she prepares to follow, she is overcome by a slight attack of faintness. "It is nothing," she tells them. "Go on in—I'll follow in a moment." They all take her at her word, but Alfredo remains behind, worried, and tells her she ought really to take better care of herself. If she would allow it, he would take care of her devotedly. "Nonsense," says she. "Does anyone really care for me?"

Alfredo takes the cue and makes the proper answer; but she only laughs at him—flirtatiously. All this takes place while the orchestra plays a nervous little waltz tune

No. 5
Allegro

—and on our larger stages, anonymous couples are seen in the background dancing together. Three-four time, in fact, dominates most of the act, one of the few essentially happy scenes Verdi ever wrote.

With his announcement that he has loved her at a distance for a whole year, the scene takes on a new earnestness. The waltz rhythm disappears, and in simple, almost hesitant accents, Alfredo tells her of the happy day (*"Un dì felice"*) he first laid eyes on her (see p. 155). In a few bars, he works up to his own love theme, which bears a striking resemblance to Violetta's heard first in the Prelude. Each is a downward scale:

Quote a & b

It is marked *con espansione*—and Alfredo expands emotionally, telling her with utter and simple conviction that his love for her now mysteriously governs his whole universe.

Slightly frightened by such sincere ardor (which apparently she had never encountered before), Violetta gaily but tenderly tells him he had better have nothing to do with her. All she can offer is a free friendship to anyone. Their voices blend —hers in gay coloratura, advising him to forget, his insisting

on the universality of his love. Gastone, in search of his hostess, briefly interrupts this duet, and we hear the waltz once more. To its tunes, she coquettishly gives Alfredo a flower from her corsage, suggesting that he go now, but return when it has died. He is delighted, for that means tomorrow.

All the guests come in now to bid their hostess good night, for it is almost morning. Left alone, Violetta has one of the best scenes ever written for a prima donna—two famous arias one right after the other, and no one to share bows with. Many sopranos, however, use them merely as show pieces, giving no hint that they express perfectly the striking contrast between awakening true love and the feverish excitement that is characteristic of the rest of Violetta's life.

The first aria, *"Ah, fors' è lui"* ("Could it be he?"), is preceded by her freshly born wonder as to whether true love might not be worth while. Alfredo's obvious sincerity has aroused a strange sensation. The aria itself starts gently in minor, then broadens out into the same major melody and words Alfredo had used in telling of his own discovery of love (see p. 161). Violetta, being in reality a deeper and more complex character than Alfredo, goes on, in a repetition of the minor-major contrast, to say that this power is gaining over her even against her will. Taking vigorous hold of herself, however, she looks reality in the face. With no real friends in this great city of Paris, what can her career be? Pleasure, and pleasure alone. With that she bursts into the second aria, *"Sempre libera"* ("Always free"), a wild expression of her feverish health and life (see p. 164). But off stage, under her balcony, Alfredo interrupts with his tender, passionate love melody. For a moment she listens, and then with a cry of "What folly!" again sings her brilliant paean to pleasure. When Alfredo's voice is heard once more, it is used only for her to build upon it wilder and wilder decorative scales and trills expressive of her conviction that life must hold nothing but superficial joys for one like her. And on this note the first act ends.

Act Two, Scene 1

IN Dumas's play, there is a second act in which Violetta gives in to Alfredo's pleadings; but opera must always condense the action of a play on which it is based, and the second act of *La Traviata* finds the lovers comfortably ensconced in Violetta's house in Auteuil, a suburb of Paris. Verdi laid the scene in a room off the garden in this house, but most modern productions place it in the garden itself, with a writing table on one side of a flower bed. Here we find Alfredo in riding breeches (Verdi asked for a hunting costume), telling of the complete happiness he has known for the past three months, since they have lived here. His ideal of love, of which he sang in the first act, has been more than realized ever since the day that Violetta herself suggested that they live together. Somehow, this aria, *"De' miei bollenti spiriti"* ("From my wild spirit"), seldom comes off so successfully on the stage as it

ought to. I suspect that Verdi—a highly moral gentleman— had a feeling of contempt for Alfredo. At any rate, the tenor's most effective music always comes in concert with Violetta.

Annina, the maidservant, punctuates Alfredo's self-felicitation with the announcement that she is going to Paris. Her mission is a secret, but it takes almost no prompting for her to reveal that Violetta has sent her to dispose of everything she owns. It is expensive to live like this, says Annina, and Violetta owes a thousand louis (roughly, six thousand dollars).

Alfredo is aghast. Apparently he had never thought about who was paying the bills. He tells Annina not to mention it to his mistress, but he is going right off to Paris himself to rectify this error. Not, however, before he has given expression to his remorse in an aria so conventional that it is usually omitted completely. And off he dashes—still in riding breeches.

Almost as soon as Alfredo has left the stage, Violetta comes into the garden—a vastly different Violetta from the one who sang *"Sempre libera."* Instead of the latest (1840) and most daring Parisian evening dress, she wears a simple country frock. Gone are the feverish manner and the fashionable hairdo—and with them the brilliant coloratura music. From this point on, the soprano who sings the role must rely on her capacity for conveying emotion through melody and effective acting, not through high notes and trills.

Violetta is obviously the business head of this household, for she at once starts dealing with the bills and papers she brings with her and is surprised to learn from Annina that Alfredo has gone off. A manservant now enters with an invitation from her Parisian friend, Flora Bervoix, to a party that evening, but Violetta has no interest in such affairs now. She is expecting her own business agent this morning, and leaves instructions that he be admitted at once.

A visitor comes almost immediately, but it is not her agent, as she first supposes. It is a dignified, elderly gentleman who introduces himself as the father of Alfredo, that wild young fellow she is ruining. Apparently a certain amount of caddishness runs in the Germont family. Violetta, however, behaves herself with such modest dignity that the old man is impressed. He is even more impressed when she proves to him, with her papers, that Alfredo is not the one who is being ruined.

The scene that follows (see p. 169) is based on very simple and universal emotions, and it is almost impossible not to be moved by Verdi's musical expression of them. On the other hand, it is also a scene that drama lovers may scoff at as hopelessly old-fashioned and hammy, for the social values (as opposed to the eternal emotional ones) on which it is predicated are those of another day and another country. We must remember that both Violetta and Germont had a far narrower view of the sanctity of family name and conventions than is current on the American stage, and that Violetta understood the force of Germont's arguments with a more natural sympathy than we can give them, for at bottom she had the same ideals.

Despite his quickly found respect for her character, Germont at once proceeds to convince Violetta of the necessity of giving up Alfredo for his own sake. His first argument—that her past stands in the way—she dismisses quickly by saying that that is all over. Germont agrees, but he has more powerful weapons. Alfredo, in over three months of intimacy, has apparently never told Violetta a thing about his family, and Germont—in the first of the beautiful melodies that stud this scene—tells her of Alfredo's young sister, who cannot hope for marriage while Alfredo is carrying on his affair. "I understand," says Violetta. "You want us to part until she is married. It will be hard, but I'll do it."

That is not enough for Germont. It must be forever, he says. With the rise of her feverishness depicted in the music, Violetta says that this is asking too much. Alfredo is the only person who can love and protect her, and she is ill with a fatal illness. Rather, she says in accents that rise in passion and conviction, would she die.

Germont's next argument, couched in a rather conventional Verdian minor melody, carries more weight because Violetta recognizes its psychological soundness. The present bliss she enjoys, says Germont, can be only temporary, for men are fickle, and no law or ceremony has sanctified her union. Violetta keeps muttering, "True, that's true;" for however much she loves Alfredo, she does seem to be fully aware of his fundamental weakness of character. And when Germont repeats his plea on behalf of his daughter, she is won over—and utterly grief-stricken. In a minor and distorted version of Alfredo's love theme (see p. 171), she gives in completely, blaming not

Alfredo or his father, but the misery of the circumstances and man's unforgiving nature. Pulling herself together for a moment, she asks Germont to tell his daughter of this sacrifice she is ready to make.

Germont's respect and compassion for Violetta rise with everything she says. He praises her generosity, but the only genuine comfort he can offer is the assurance that her deed will carry its own reward, that heaven will remember it. Just how she plans to break with Alfredo, she will not tell him— and in a long and tearful leave-taking, they embrace and part.

There is no hesitation now on Violetta's part. She sits down to write Flora an acceptance of her invitation to the party, rings for Annina, who is surprised when she reads the address, and then sits down to compose a farewell to Alfredo.

In the midst of it, she is surprised by Alfredo's return. She hides the letter from him nervously, but he is too full of his own troubles to be more than casually curious. It seems that Germont had left a severely reprimanding letter for him before the interview with Violetta. Immediately brushing her own far greater sorrow aside, Violetta assumes charge of the situation, promising that she herself will fall at Germont's feet and ask for his forgiveness. But the effort at deception is just a little too much for her. Even the obtuse lover sees that she is upset when in a breathless, mounting musical phrase she asks over and over again whether he does not really love her. The great and most moving climax of the act comes here. To quiet but insistent little trills in the orchestra, she tells him she is over her nervousness and will await him and his father among the flowers in the garden. Then, with a tremendous crescendo in the orchestra, she passionately sings the love melody of the Prelude: *"Amami, Alfredo; amami quant 'io t 'amo"* ("Love me, Alfredo; love me as much as I do you").

Violetta goes out, and Alfredo reflects with self-satisfaction that this devoted heart is certainly in love with him. The male servant interrupts him with the news that Violetta and Annina have left for Paris in a coach, but Alfredo sees nothing more in that than the probability of her having gone to sell her belongings to pay the household bills. He is quickly enlightened by the delivery of Violetta's note announcing very briefly that they have now parted. He can barely utter his astonishment when Germont re-enters and, in the most familiar if not the finest music of the act, tries to comfort his son. He sings the aria *"Di Provenza"* ("From Provence"), in which he recalls their once happy home in the south of France, where Alfredo should return to ease his pain (see p. 177). Alfredo listens with the ill-restrained impatience of the leading tenor listening to the baritone having his best aria.

When it is over, Alfredo has found a reason for Violetta's departure. It is, he thinks, to go to meet Baron Douphol—and now his only thought is revenge. Germont renews his appeal to return home in another rather commonplace aria (regularly omitted in American performances); but Alfredo, catching sight of Flora's invitation, which Violetta has left on the writing table, reads it, pushes his father aside, and rushes off.

Act Two, Scene 2*

FLORA BERVOIX is giving a party. She is expecting Violetta to show up with Alfredo, but the Marquis d'Obigny has already heard the gossip, and, as the curtain goes up on Flora's rather showy party room, he is telling his hostess that if Violetta comes at all, it will be with the Baron Douphol.

This party—to distinguish it in spirit from Violetta's in Act I—is supposed to be a masquerade, to which most of the guests come arrayed as either gypsies or matadors. As given today, however, the gypsies and matadors are members of the ballet, who dance while the chorus—dressed as it was in Act I— does the singing. The words, which in the first person plural praise the life of the gypsy, do not make much sense in the mouths of fashionable folk of nineteenth-century Paris; but as no one is expected to understand them, that does not make much difference, while it gives opportunity for the ballet troupe to enliven the proceedings. One of the tunes sung during the ballet bears a striking resemblance to the nervous little waltz in Act I. The resemblance may be purely accidental, but one can suspect a purpose behind it, for it is further developed more dramatically a little while later.

Alfredo—who, it will be remembered, received no invitation to the party but was expected to come as Violetta's escort— now enters alone, admits that he has parted with her, and at once sits down at the gambling table on one side of the stage. He plays with Gastone and others, winning each time, and repeating the trite observation "Lucky at cards, unlucky at love." Meantime Violetta enters on the arm of Baron Douphol, who immediately spies Alfredo at the card table and warns Violetta not to speak to him. The whole gambling scene is accompanied in the orchestra by the insistent but subdued repetition of a theme again closely akin to the nervous little waltz tune of Act I.

No. 6
Allegro agitato

ppp

It is rescued from monotony by a broad melodic phrase that Violetta sings at three different points, expressing a sense of impending doom.

No. 7
Allegro

What will they do? I feel like dy-ing, Dear God have mer-cy on me, dear God!
Che fi - a? mo - rir mi sen-to! pie - tà, gran Dio, pietà, gran Dio, di me!

---

*It is customary today to give *La Traviata* in four acts, the present scene being called Act III and the following act, Act IV. The score, however, calls this scene Act II, Scene 2, and so do a minority of our present-day programs and all of our phonograph recordings.

Douphol, though he has forbidden Violetta to speak to Alfredo, challenges the young man to play and in two turns of the cards loses three hundred louis (about eighteen hundred dollars). The game is interrupted by the announcement that supper is ready, but the Baron is quite ready to accept Alfredo's invitation to revenge, the hint of an impending duel over more than the three hundred louis being quite apparent in Alfredo's language.

As the guests go off, Violetta sends Flora after Alfredo to come to speak to her a moment, and he returns to find her extremely agitated and asking him to leave before the challenge becomes explicit. Alfredo scorns this course as unworthy of a hotheaded, jealous male, but promises to go if she will follow him immediately. That, she says, she cannot do on account of a promise she has made. Immediately Alfredo assumes it must be Douphol to whom she has made this promise, and he asks her point-blank whether she loves him. Seeing no way out, Violetta says she does, and Alfredo dramatically summons the entire company. In accents of mounting disdain and passion, he tells them that he had foolishly accepted her bounty, but that now, when he has found out her true character, he repays the debt—and he flings his winnings violently at Violetta's feet, while she faints away in Flora's arms. These juvenile melodramatics are more than the company can stomach. They turn on Alfredo unanimously and tell him he had better leave at once.

Germont enters at this moment, turning up for dramatic rather than logical reasons. He sees his son's performance and, in an effective but rather grandiose manner, disowns him publicly. A magnificent concerted number brings the act to a dramatic close. All the principals and the chorus sing at once, and it becomes difficult to disentangle the words, though their purport is obvious enough. Alfredo is covered with shame and grief over having now lost Violetta permanently; Germont says that he knows the true worth of Violetta's faithfulness but that nevertheless the lovers must part; Douphol challenges Alfredo to a duel to take place as soon as possible; while the rest express sympathy for Violetta. Violetta herself recovers enough to utter a touching little melody in which she tells Alfredo (who doesn't seem to hear it) that she acted only on account of her love for him. The conflicting emotions expressed simultaneously rise to a great volume of sound that fills the house with passionate music. It is a typical Verdi climax with a dozen different vocal lines. The curtain falls as Douphol flings a challenging glove at the feet of Alfredo, who picks it up and stalks out followed by his father.

Act Three

ALL stage directors do not follow Verdi's effective directions at the opening of this act, which are to disclose the scene before the Prelude, not after it. It is Violetta's bedroom in a dilapidated house in Paris. The curtains are half drawn on the bed in which she lies asleep, and Annina, also asleep, is seated by the fireplace. There they remain while the orchestra plays the Prelude.

It begins, like the Prelude to Act I, with divided strings softly suggesting Violetta's fatal illness. The violins sing a pathetic melody which Violetta takes up later in the act. It is in a major key and brings up in her mind the relief from pain that comes with prayer. The brief Prelude ends with a series of dying sobs suggestive of Violetta's ebbing strength.

When Violetta wakes, she calls for water, and to short strains from the Prelude we learn that it is eight in the morning, and that the Doctor is downstairs. He enters almost at

once, gives his patient some professional cheer which she is wise enough to discount, and leaves, telling Annina under his breath that it is now only a matter of hours.

A not entirely convincing bit of pathos follows, in which Violetta sends Annina out to distribute ten of her remaining twenty louis to be given to the poor. Seated by the little table and looking deathly ill, Violetta draws a worn letter from her bosom and reads it softly—speaking, not singing—against the pianissimo playing on a single violin of Alfredo's love theme accompanied by tremolo strings. The letter is from Germont: *"You have kept your promise. The duel took place. The Baron was wounded and is getting better. Alfredo is in a foreign country. I myself have told him of your sacrifice. He will return to you to sue for a pardon, and I shall come with him. . . ."*

The letter, Violetta complains, came a long time ago, but still they don't come;* and now, gazing at her wasted face in the mirror, she knows that there is not much time left for her. She sings, then, the most pathetic aria in this most pathetic of operas—*"Addio del passato"*—her farewell to the world and to love (see p. 180). It is made particularly telling by a change from minor to major as she thinks of the hope of a life after death (Violetta is *always* hoping) and by her breaking off in the song now and again from weakness, while the oboe takes up the melody.

A bacchanalian chorus of early-morning revelers passes the window by way of contrast, and Annina returns with great news. For a moment she is so shocked by Violetta's appearance that she is afraid to give it. Her mistress, however, reads it at once on her face: Alfredo has come. The young man bursts into the room, and the lovers throw themselves ecstatically into each other's arms.

*The libretto does not say how long she has been waiting, but in Dumas's play it is six weeks.

Their initial rapture over, they sing the affecting duet *"Parigi, o cara,"* in which they plan to leave Paris and live for love alone (see p. 183). It is only when this duet is over, and Violetta, exhausted by emotion, sinks weakly to the couch, that Alfredo notices she is not well. Violetta, however, pulls herself together and asks Annina for a dress. The effort of putting it on is too much. Alfredo sends Annina for the Doctor, but Violetta knows it is too late now and tells Alfredo. If that is so, he says in the continuation of their duet, he will die with her. The Doctor and Germont come in, and the father takes Violetta to his breast, at last repenting his cruelty.

The stage is now set for the final concerted number. Violetta takes a small picture of herself from a casket and gives it to Alfredo, suggesting that if he should marry a modest girl, he should give it to her as a token from one who prays for both of them from Heaven. The idea strikes a modern hearer as on the morbid side, not to mention the embarrassment it might mean to Alfredo. Its essential generosity, however, brings forth from him the conflicting statements that he cannot part from her yet, that she isn't going to die anyway, and that he will die with her. Annina, Germont, and the Doctor join in with expressions of sorrow and admiration for Violetta's pure spirit in a simple and affecting quintet.

At its close, Violetta experiences a transfiguring euphoria. High up, as softly as possible (*pppp*), the violins play Alfredo's love theme, while she tells them in a speaking voice that all her faintness and pains are gone. For a moment she imagines that her life is returning. "Oh, joy!" she cries—and falls back on the sofa. As the Doctor pronounces her dead, the curtain falls, her remorseful lover and his father stricken with grief.

Prelude

slowly dying away

Drinking Song
LIBIAMO, LIBIAMO

Original key: B-flat

sum - mer ___ skies. ___ Drink deep - ly, drink
ten - te ___ va. ___ Li - bia - mo, a -

deep - ly to life ___ and love, ___ and the bright - ness ___ that
mo - re, a - mor fra i ca - li - ci più cal - di

ALL

shines in ___ her ___ eyes. Ah! ___ to life and ___ love and
ba - ci a - vrà. Ah! ___ li - biam, a - mor fra'

beau - ty ___ and the light that ___ shines in ___ her ___ eyes.
ca - li - ci più cal - di ba - cia - vrà.

The Day I Met You

UN DÌ FELICE

Andantine

Original key: F

The day I met you, O bless-ed day, When first you
Un dì fe-li-ce, e-te-re-a mi ba-le-

came be-fore ____ me, When I be-held ____ a
na-ste in-nan-te, e da quel dì ____ tre-

vis-ion, Dreamed of the love yet to be,
man-te vis-si d'i-gno-to a-mor.

Dreamed of a love that would fill my life for me, Love that would
Di quel-l'a-mor, quel-l'a-mor ch'è pal-pi-to del-l'u-ni-

ban-ish the world and all its mad-ness, Mys-tic and ho-ly,
ver-so, del-l'u-ni-ver-so in-te-ro, mi-ste-ri-o-so,

blend-ing both joy and sad-ness, Ho-ly, mys-tic and ho-ly hap-py and
mi-ste-ri-o-so al-te-ro, cro-ce, cro-ce e de-li-zia cro-ce e de-

VIOLETTA

ho-ly, hap-py and free. Real-ly my friend, you fright-en me!
li-zia, de-li-zia al cor. Ah, se ciò è ver, fug-gi-te-mi!

) 156 (

brightly and lightly

You must not dare to love me; Your love _____ is far a-
So-lo a-mi-sta-de io v'of-fro; a-mar _____ non so, nè

bove _____ me, A - las ____ I ____ fear you must for - get ____ me.
sof - - fro un - co - sì e - roi-co a - mo - re.

Mine is a heart for light - er love, I must be free to
Io so - no fran - ca in - ge - nu - a, al - tra cer - car do -

wan - der, I pray _____ you not to ___ squan - - der your
ve - te, non ar - - duo tro - ve - re - - te di -

Ah!
Ah!

Ah!
Ah!

Ah! _____ such love can nev - er ____ be! _____
Ah! _____ di - men - ti - car-mi al - lor! _____

Ah! _____ that love like this might ____ be! _____
Ah! _____ croce_e de - li-zia_al cor! _____

Ah, Can It Be

AH, FORS' È LUI

Original key: F minor

Andantino

_p_ L.H. leggiero _pp_

_p_ VIOLETTA (sweetly and softly)

Ah, can it be that this is he Of whom my heart fore - told me,
Ah, for - s'è lui che l'a - ni - ma so - lin - ga ne' tu - mul - ti,

of whom my dream fore - warned me. Is his the love to set me
so - lin - ga ne' tu - mul - ti, go - dea so - ven - te pin - ge -

free, Love that will sure - ly hold me when all the world has scorned me.
re de suoi co - lo - ri_oc - cul - ti, de suoi co - lo - ri_oc - cul - ti.

He who has sweet - ly shown to me sym - pa - thy in my weak - ness,
Lui, che mo - de - sto_e vi - gi - le al - l'e - gre so - glie_a - sce - se,

He who at last makes known to me, All that my love could be.
e nuo - va feb - bre_ac - ce - se, de - stan - do - mi_al - l'a - mor!

Here is a love that could fill_____ my life for me,
A quel - l'a - mor, quel - l'a - mor_____ ch'è pal - pi - to

Love that would ban - ish the world and all_ its mad - ness,
del - l'u - ni - ver - so, del - l'u - ni - ver - so_in - te - ro,

Mys - tic and ho - ly, Blend - ing both joy and
mi - ste - ri - o - so, mi - ste - ri - o - so al-

sad - ness Ho - ly, mys-tic and ho - ly, ho - ly and
te - ro, cro - ce, cro-ce e de - li - zia, cro-ce e de-

hap - py, hap-py and free! Mys-tic and ho - ly hap-py and free!
li - zia, de li-zia al cor! cro-ce e de - li - zia, de-li-zia al cor!

Ah!_____ hap-py and free.
Ah!_____ de - li-zia al cor!

Ever Free
SEMPRE LIBERA

Original key: A-flat

free to take — my chanc - es in the game of fol - ly and plea - sure, When they
li - be - ra — deg - g'i - o fol - leg - gia - re di gio-ja_in gio - ja, vo' che

start the songs — and danc - es I'll be there to play — my part. When the
scor - ra_il vi - ver mi - o pei sen - tie - ri del — pia - cer. Nas-ca_il

Love____ calls____ my heart,
dee____ vo - lar__ il pen - sier,

Love calls to
A - mor è

In____ my____ heart,
dee____ vo - - lar,

in____ my____
dee____ vo - -

all of us,
pal - pi-to,

calls us to rap - ture!
del - l'u - ni - ver - so!

heart.____
lar.____

Love _____ calls my heart, my _____ fool - ish
dee _____ vo - lar, il _____ mio pen -

heart, my _____ wand - 'ring heart, _____
sier, il _____ mio pen - sier, _____

_____ my_ wand - - 'ring
_____ *il_ mio _____ pen -*

heart.
sier.

I Have a Daughter

PURA SICCOME

Original key: A-flat

Some day this ten - der child____ of mine, Ea - ger for life's com -
l'a - ma-to ea-man - te gio - - vi - ne cui spo-sa an-dar do -

plete - ness, Must be the bride of some good man__ and__
ve - a, or si ri-cu-sa al vin - co - lo che__

leave the_home she filled with sweet - ness. Love is a rose that
lie - ti,_ lie - ti ne ren - de - va. Deh, non mu - ta - te in

blooms for her, Un - der a cloud - less sky. Will you con-demn this
tri - bo-li le ro - se del - l'a - mor. Ah non mu - ta - te in

ten - der thing to fade a - way and die? I beg you, ask your
tri - bo - li le ro - se del - l'a - mor, a prie - ghi miei re -

heart, if such a thing should be and let your heart re - ply.
si - ste - re no, no, non vo - glia il vo - stro cor, no, no.

Andante più mosso
VIOLETTA (in agony of grief)

Ah, what a death for my love just a -
Co - si al - la mi - se - ra, ch'è un dì ca -

wak - ing! Where is the hope for a
du - ta, di più ri - sor - ge - re

One rose that prom - ised to blos - som a -
che a lei il sa - cri - fi - ca e che mor -

know how your no - ble
pe - - - - ne, co - rag - gio, e il

gain All in vain, all in vain!
rà, e mor - rà, e mor - rà,

heart must be feel - ing this pain! Heav - en, heav - en,
no - bi - le cor vin - ce - rà! Pian - gi, pian - gi,

Ah, rose that bloomed a - gain, but all in
A lei il sa - cri - fi - ca e mor -

Heav - en grant you strength to bear your bur - den of sor - row and
pian - gi, o mi - se - ra! co - rag - gio, e il no - bi - le cor vin - ce -

sempre cantando

vain.
rà,

Ah,
a

rose___ that bloomed a -
lei_____ il sa -

pain! Heav - en,   Heav - en,   Heav - en grant   you   strength   to   bear   your
rà. Pian - gi,   pian - gi,   pian-gi, o   mi - se - ra!   co - rag - gio, e il

gain,   but   all   in   vain.   Blos-somed a - gain,   blos - somed in
cri - fi - ca e   mor - rà,   e   che mor - rà,   e   che mor -

bur - den_ of _sor - row and   pain!   May Heav - en   strength - en your
no - bi - le _cor vin - ce - rà,   co - rag - gio,   e il   no - bil

vain,   oh,__ heart__ that loved a - gain, all   in   vain!
rà,   e mor - rà,_____ e   che mor - rà, che   mor - rà.

heart,   may your heart, ah may your heart be strong through its pain!
cor vin - ce - rà, ah sì, il no - bil cor vin - ce - rà.

) 176 (

In Provence

DI PROVENZA

Original key: D-flat

In Pro - vence the southern sea   soft-ly   cools the sun-lit shore,   Oh the
Di Pro - ven-za il mar, il suol   chi dal   cor   ti can-cel - lò?   chi dal

peace-ful   sun - lit   shore   of   Pro - vence be - side   the   sea!   And the
cor   ti   can-cel - lò   di Pro - ven-za il mar,   il   suol?   Al   na -

bright un-cloud-ed sun shines as warm-ly as be-fore, Just as
tio ful-gen-te sol qual de-sti-no ti fu-rò? Qual de-

when you lived be-fore In the bright un-cloud-ed sun. Though it
sti - no ti fu - rò al na-tio ful-gen - te sol? Oh ram-

seems that love is done, That this ache will nev-er cease, Just re-
men - ta pur nel duol ch'i - vi gio-ja a te bril - lò, e che

Ped.

mem-ber, O my son, there at home is light and peace, Just re-
pa - ce co - là sol su te splen - de - re an-cor può, e che

Ped.

So Closes My Sad Story

ADDIO DEL PASSATO

Original key: A minor

gray._____ I long for his voice, would to God I might
len - - ti; l'a - mo - re d'Al - fre - do per - fi - no mi

hear it To strength - en my heart and to com - fort my
man - ca, con - for - to, so - ste - gno del - l'a - ni - ma

spir-it,_____ to_____ com-fort
stan-ca,_____ con - for-to,

my_____ heart. Ah, fare-well,_____ Tra - via-ta,_____ Oh_____
so - ste - gno. Ah! del - la _____ Tra - via-ta _____ sor -

la - dy_____ of_____ laugh - ter, May God____ grant in__ His__
ri - di_____ al de - si____ - o, a le - i deh per -

mer - cy, a bless - ed here - af-ter!
do - na, tu ac - co - gli-la, o Di - o!

Life____ and__ love__ are gone, are__ gone! I_____ go a -
Ah,_____ tut - to,____ tut - to__ fi - nì, or____ tut - -

lone, Life__ and__ love are_____ gone!
to, tut - - to fi - nì!

We'll Find a Haven

PARIGI, O CARA

Original key: A-flat

Andante mosso ... **VIOLETTA** *(softly, intimately)*

We'll find a ha — ven
Pa - ri - gi, o ca - ra

you and I to - geth — er, Where skies are fair in bright sum - mer
noi — la - sce - re — mo, la — vi - ta u - ni - ti tra - scor - re —

weath — er; Sor - row and sad — ness shall — be for - got - ten,
re — mo de' — cor - si af - fan — ni com - pen - so a - vra — i,

Your love shall make me hap-py and strong. With you to
la mia sa - lu - te ri - fio - ri - rà. *So - spi - ro e*

ALFREDO

With
So -

love me, with you be-side me, Life will be bright-er,
lu - ce tu mi sa - ra - i, tut - to il fu - tu - ro

me, with me, with me!
spir, lu - ce sa - rai.

sweet as a song. Yes, all my
ne ar - ri - de - rà. *De' cor - si af-*

Far from the cit - y We'll find a ha - ven!
Pa - ri - gi, o ca - ra, noi la - sce - re - mo,

) 184 (

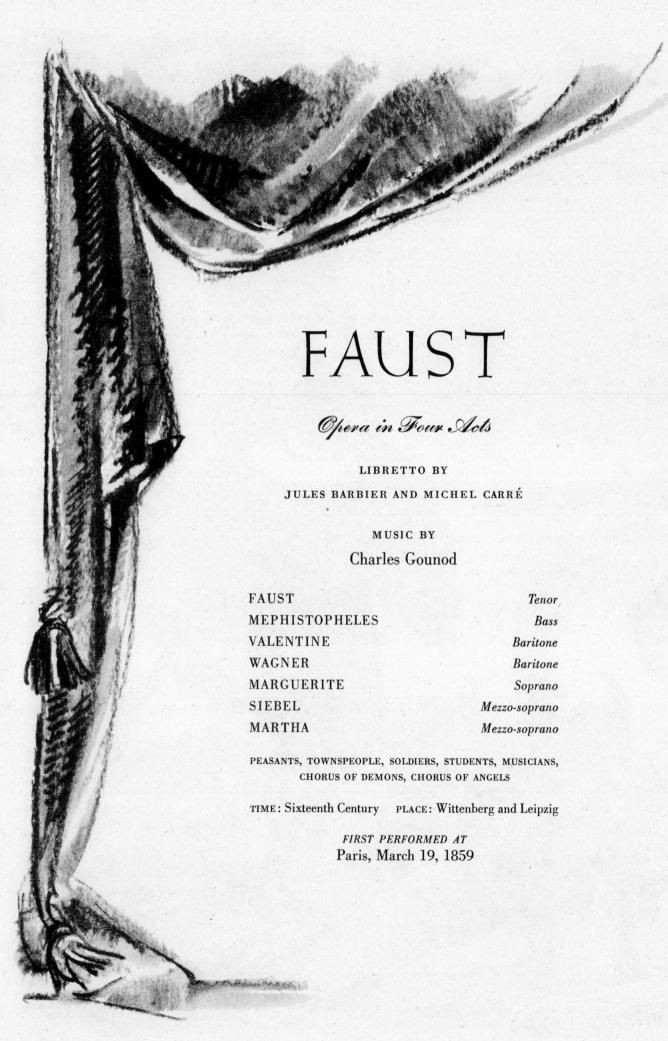

FAUST

Opera in Four Acts

LIBRETTO BY

JULES BARBIER AND MICHEL CARRÉ

MUSIC BY

Charles Gounod

FAUST	*Tenor*
MEPHISTOPHELES	*Bass*
VALENTINE	*Baritone*
WAGNER	*Baritone*
MARGUERITE	*Soprano*
SIEBEL	*Mezzo-soprano*
MARTHA	*Mezzo-soprano*

PEASANTS, TOWNSPEOPLE, SOLDIERS, STUDENTS, MUSICIANS,
CHORUS OF DEMONS, CHORUS OF ANGELS

TIME: Sixteenth Century   PLACE: Wittenberg and Leipzig

FIRST PERFORMED AT
Paris, March 19, 1859

Faust

CHARLES GOUNOD

WHEN the Germans put on Gounod's opera *Faust*, they advertise it as *Margarete*. One reason is that Goethe's play, *Faust*, may occupy the same stage another night in the same week. Another reason is the great respect they have for their national poet and their resentment that a Frenchman should have composed the most successful of the many operatic treatments his masterwork has had. The change in title really constitutes a trenchant critical comment on the libretto.

This libretto, written by the successful French dramatist Jules Barbier,* has in it practically none of the philosophical significance of Goethe's poem, which deals with the problems of good and evil and ends, in Part II, with the triumph of good. Barbier's Faust stops being a philosopher promptly after the first ten minutes of singing, and during those first ten minutes he complains more than he philosophizes.

The central figure in the opera is really Marguerite, and Marguerite is a figure invented by Goethe. She does not appear in the sixteenth-century Spiess biography of Dr. Faustus or in Marlowe or in the medieval puppet plays, or in any part of the twenty-eight versions of the story that appeared during the sixty years Goethe was working on his poem. It is therefore unnecessary here to go into a discussion of the literary history of the Faust legend. All we need to do is to see how Carré treated Goethe's *Faust,* and the character of Marguerite particularly.

Goethe's *Faust* is, of course, generally acknowledged to be one of the great masterpieces of world literature. Nevertheless, outside of its native country, it is seldom accorded a stage performance, for Goethe's genius was not essentially dramatic. From the point of view of dramatic action—and especially operatic action—Barbier made his version worthy of the literally thousands of performances it has achieved by summarily cutting

out all the purely philosophical dialogue, compressing the action, bringing the scenes down to a reasonable number, adding a few original and effective touches, and making of Marguerite an essentially more sympathetic character. This is not to say that it would hold the stage without Gounod's music; but Barbier was writing a libretto for an opera, not a play of spoken verses. As such, it is highly successful.

Marguerite is essentially the figure Goethe created—a peasant girl, simple and direct. The simplicity and directness of the opera's heroine, however, are greater than her originals. She does not pester her lover about his religion. She accepts him as he is. Nor does she descend to giving her mother a sleeping potion so that she and Faust may make love undisturbed. Barbier avoids that unpleasantness by making an orphan of her. Finally, Barbier's Marguerite is not coy. She does not lead Faust on, finally giving in after a long suit. Instead, she succumbs the very first night in a transport of ecstasy, without planning, without misgiving. Berlioz chose that passage ("*Il m'aime*," at the end of the garden scene) as the finest in the opera.

Faust and Mephistopheles are not improved on in the same way. Rather, they lose in depth—necessarily, because their excuse for being in Goethe lies largely in their philosophical discourses, not in their actions. Faust, particularly, becomes a two-dimensional figure, a conventional operatic tenor. In Goethe, Faust does not gain real moral stature before Part II anyway, and the opera deals only with Part I.

The action follows Goethe's play closely, though with many skips. On account of this closeness, in the pages that follow I have taken the liberty of being more specific in a few places than the libretto is. For instance, Goethe tells us, as Barbier does not, what book Faust is reading in the first scene—the *Prophecies of Nostradamus*. Marguerite's home, too, is specifically Leipzig in Goethe but only "a small German town" in Barbier.

The idea of writing music for Goethe's *Faust* fascinated Gounod many years before he started working on it. It is a theme that has fascinated many musicians—

---

*Michel Carré is always given credit for having written the text with Barbier. Though Carré was commissioned to do so, he was unenthusiastic over the idea because he had already written a play on the subject. His contributions to the opera, says Ernest Newman, include only the texts of two numbers—Marguerite's "King of Thule" and Mephisto's "Calf of Gold."

Schumann, Liszt, Wagner, Spohr, Berlioz, Boito, to name the first that come to mind. Beethoven and Meyerbeer both considered it. Gounod, however, took the idea really seriously only after a conversation with Barbier—or maybe it was with Carvalho, director of the Théâtre-Lyrique in Paris. All three men wrote accounts of the genesis of the idea, each claiming credit for himself. It makes little difference who had the idea first: all three collaborated, Barbier by supplying the libretto, Gounod by writing the music, Carvalho by offering to produce it.

Gounod and Barbier began work in 1857, but halfway through the composition news came that the Théâtre Porte Saint-Martin was putting on a *Faust* by one Dennery. As this theater was better equipped for spectacular effects than the Lyrique, Carvalho hesitated to compete and commissioned the disappointed author and composer to write instead a comic opera based on Molière's *Doctor in Spite of Himself*.

Dennery's *Faust,* however, was a failure, and on March 19, 1859, the Théâtre-Lyrique produced Gounod's opera, the greatest popular success Gounod or any other French composer ever had. It was given not as we hear it today, but as an *opéra comique*—that is, with spoken dialogue. It was not until 1869 that music was added for the recitatives and the ballet music inserted for the production at the Paris Grand Opéra.

The 1859 *première* had Mme. Carvalho as Marguerite and Balanqué as Mephistopheles, both of whom, Gounod tells us in his *Memoirs*, were wonderfully well cast, despite a tendency to overact on the part of the basso. Barbot, a middle-aged tenor, was not quite equal to the demands of the title role, and at one point in the rehearsals Gounod seriously considered taking over the part himself. He liked his own little voice.

It is sometimes said that the opera at first was a failure. The number of recorded performances in the first season belie this statement, but it was only slowly that the work achieved its enormous popularity. The Paris Grand Opéra, since 1869, has given well over two thousand performances; the Metropolitan's score is pushing hard on to three hundred; and at one point in the history of that institution it was given so often that the late William Henderson referred to the house on Thirty-ninth Street as *Das Faustspielhaus*.

In 1863 it was introduced to London in two different theaters, one playing it in English and the other in Italian. The same year New York also heard it for the first time—in German at one theater and in Italian at another. An Italian *Faust* was also the first opera to be performed at the Metropolitan when it opened in 1883. It is now, of course, part of the standard repertoire of every opera company in the Western world.

Gounod wrote the music soon after a severe nervous breakdown. As he tells us in his autobiography (which stops short after the production of *Faust*), it captured the imagination of the public more than anything else he wrote. Whether it is really his best, he is not so sure —but that seems to be the opinion of posterity anyway. Today it is fashionable among musical sophisticates to be condescending about it—not because it is popular (*Carmen*, which is quite as popular today, has earned itself a great deal of respect), but because its music is said to be "perfumed charm," its melodies and harmonic devices obvious.

It did not so strike the critics of the 1860's, who made almost as much fuss about Gounod as they did about Wagner. The much-maligned "Soldiers' Chorus" (originally written, by the way, for an uncompleted opera called *Ivan the Terrible*) thrilled that sour Britisher Chorley. "I shall never forget," he wrote, "the riotous enthusiasm which burst out when this magnificent chorus, to which an army of myriads might sweep on its way to victory, electrified the ears of the Théâtre-Lyrique on the night of the first performance of the opera." The love duet, he reported, was something completely new to the operatic world of its day.* But, striking and strikingly popular as many of its individual passages are, they cannot alone account for the enormous popularity of *Faust*. Only a work with something consistently great about it could survive the many thousands of performances this one has had and still sound vital and fresh enough to hold audiences everywhere almost ninety years after its *première*. Many other operas have had as great a success for a few years and then been forgotten.

---

*Of course, Chorley may be regarded as a prejudiced critic: he supplied the frightful translation used in 1864 and published ever since in the standard Schirmer edition.

Introduction

T H E slow, meditative first part of the Introduction to *Faust* and the music immediately following the rise of the curtain are the only passages in the whole opera to suggest that the tenor-hero is anything more than a conventional lover. Its uncoiling repetitions in different keys, the narrow but painful rise and fall of its themes, and the dissonances that still sound strangely modern in Gounod suggest the monotonous, involved thinking of the aged philosopher, his drab existence, his dark cell, his footless learning.

No. 1
Adagio molto

In its original form, this excellent little tone poem was followed immediately by the curtain's rising on the picture already painted in notes. But five years after the first performance, Gounod added the aria "Even Bravest Heart May Swell" to the first act of the opera so that George Santley, the popular English baritone, could have a good solo number at a London performance. It was too good a tune to use only once, and so, with true French economy, Gounod added it to the Introduction, where it is always played nowadays. It makes an effective contrast to the dark music of the first part, but completely ruins the mood setting. After the baritone aria (played by wood winds and strings), the Introduction subsides on a series of figures in triplets that are very much like the music in the off-stage chorus of happy girls later in the opening scene.

Act One, Scene 1

M O S T opera-house stages are embarrassingly large to suggest the study cell of a medieval philosopher in Wittenberg, but with the help of darkness penetrated only by a shaft of light from a window high on one side and a fireplace on the other, the effect is approached. Faust, in his black philosopher's gown and a long white beard, is seated at a study table covered with parchments, and near by on a stand is a huge open book—the *Prophecies of Nostradamus*. Music from the opening of the Introduction helps further to set the dismal tone of the picture, which is broken only when Faust starts to sing. As Faust remains an old philosopher for only a few minutes and changes into a young lover for the rest of the

evening, the part is entrusted to a lusty, young-voiced tenor whenever possible, and his voice sounds incongruously fresh.*

It is Easter morning, just before dawn, and Faust complains that all the years of his studying have taught him nothing of nature and of God. He has not even learned to die. A soft, gay tune in the orchestra suggests the coming dawn, and the light through the window grows a little brighter. "One more day," cries Faust despairingly. It is too much: he will end it—and

---

*In the performance given by the Rochester American Opera Company in 1927, two tenors took the role, one singing Faust the old man and another Faust the young. It helped only a little, for Gounod's music for the opening scene is too vigorously tenorish to be quavered.

he prepares himself a goblet of poison, singing a triumphant song in praise of his approaching end. But just as he is about to bring the goblet to his lips, he hears a chorus of girls off stage singing an early-morning song to nature and love.

No. 2
Allegretto

"All rot!" cries Faust, and with a trembling hand he raises the flask once more. Again he is interrupted by youthful voices, this time of men singing a harvest song. At its end, the girls and the men join in praise of God, and Faust echoes their words mockingly: *"Dieu! Dieu! Dieu!"*

But the suicidal mood is now broken, and he starts to curse everything good and pleasant on earth—nature, science, prayer, and faith—and ends with an invocation, calling for Satan to appear before him. A great crescendo, a crashing chord—and the Devil obliges.

His port of entry is usually the fireplace, which produces a bright red light simultaneously with the guest from hell. Mephistopheles, as he himself points out to the amazed philosopher, is dressed like a fine nobleman, a sword at his side, a plume in his hat, his purse well filled, a rich cloak over his shoulders—and all at the service of Faust. Faust is frightened at first into impoliteness: he tells Mephistopheles to get out. That, however, is no way to treat the Devil, says the fiend—to call him from such a great distance only to show him the door. Furthermore, Mephistopheles can help him to practically anything he wants—gold, glory, power.

But what Faust wants is something that promises all three of these, and more. He wants youth. He bursts into a wild and rather frank expression of just what it is he misses—young mistresses, their caresses and desires, and his own potency to satisfy them.

"Fine," says Mephistopheles, "I can get them for you." And how much will it cost? Almost nothing. Here Mephistopheles will be Faust's servant, but below (and "below" is solemnly suggested by brass instruments) it is to be vice versa.

With that, Mephistopheles offers Faust a parchment to sign; and when the old fellow still hesitates, the Devil makes a magical gesture and in the back of Faust's studio appears a vision of Marguerite at her spinning wheel. To the accompaniment of some of the music from the love scene to be heard later, Mephistopheles urges Faust to sign, and as the vision fades, the compact is sealed.

While the love music is still playing, Mephistopheles invites Faust to partake of a brightly fizzling drink he has just mixed, and Faust is quickly transformed into a handsome young tenor in tights. The transformation is accomplished by the singer's going behind Faust's high-backed chair, shedding his philosopher's robe and part of his make-up and springing forth in his newly revealed glory. There are usually some irreverent souls in the house who giggle at this.

Once more Faust sings of his wild desires, Mephistopheles this time echoing every one of his thoughts. It is one of the few places in the score where Gounod has not skillfully balanced the orchestra with the singers: for the violins play Faust's melody with him, and as the melody is a quick one, the audience seldom hears the singers before the very last phrase. Losing no time at all in their search for pleasure, the two run off the stage as the curtain falls.

Act One, Scene 2*

FROM Wittenberg, Mephistopheles transports Faust to Leipzig, where a kermesse, or fair, is noisily going on as the curtain rises. An obscure young student named Wagner (who plays an important role in some versions of the Faust legend) leads his fellow baritones in a jolly tune praising light wines and beer, the soldiers (basses) following them with the soldierly sentiment that ancient towns and young girls surrender with equal ease to valor. The bearded burghers (first tenors) then croak that what they like best of a Sunday or holiday is to sit on the banks and watch life go by (see p. 203). Young girls (first sopranos) point out that young students (second tenors) are trying to flirt with them, while the boys answer a moment later that the facts are exactly vice versa. Then the matrons (second sopranos) observe, to the same tune, that if the boys had any taste they'd change the direction of their glances and look at the matrons. Finally, the entire population voices these differing attitudes toward life simultaneously, the drinking song of the students dominating. It is an excellent example of Gounod's skill in counterpoint, but an under-rehearsed chorus makes it sound frightful.

Marguerite's brother, Valentine, another creation of Goethe's, wanders disconsolately into the midst of this jolly afternoon. Valentine is a soldier (usually dressed better than the other soldiers on the stage, but only because he is a principal singer, not because he has any higher military rank), and Wagner teases him for looking so sour over the prospect of marching off to battle. It is his orphaned sister Marguerite, says Valentine, who makes him sad: she will be left uncared for. Siebel, Marguerite's extremely youthful admirer (the part is written for a mezzo-soprano), assures Valentine that he will look after her in his stead, and several other young men also volunteer for the same attractive assignment. Slightly cheered, Valentine sings his big aria, "Even Bravest Heart May Swell" (see p. 207). The familiar melody is first accompanied by repeated triplets in the strings (a favorite device of Gounod's); a contrasting martial passage follows, and then the principal melody is repeated once more, this time with a

---

*The kermesse scene is labeled Act II in the score but Act I, Scene 2, in most programs, thus making a four-act opera out of a five-act one and saving one intermission.

wood-wind obbligato and tremolo strings accompanying. Most baritones end an octave higher than the score calls for, and some even interject a high A flat.

Wagner brings back the holiday spirit of the afternoon by proposing drinks, getting up on the table and starting the "Song of the Rat." It begins in a rousing, humorous fashion, and I have always regretted that Gounod did not permit it to get beyond the first couplet. However, Mephistopheles suddenly appears and with Gallic politeness offers to follow Wagner with another song. "One song's enough," says Wagner. "Let's see if you're any good."

Mephistopheles is. He bursts into "The Calf of Gold" in praise of that idol, describing how everyone dances about its pedestal while Satan leads them on. Satan, in this case, does lead them on, for the soldiers and students join lustily in the chorus without understanding its irreligious connotations. Only Valentine has some suspicions about this gay stranger, but Wagner invites Mephistopheles to have a drink—just to show he bears no hard feelings. Mephistopheles accepts but seizes Wagner's hand, points to the life line on the palm, and predicts that the young man will lose his life in battle. (Apparently it is a sound prediction: Wagner disappears from the opera thereafter.) Siebel, the foolish boy, asks to have his fortune read too, and learns that any flower he touches hereafter will wither at once. No more bouquets, adds the Devil, for Marguerite. Valentine objects to hearing his sister's name bandied about this way; but Mephistopheles, without even bothering to inspect his palm, predicts that the soldier also will be killed —and by someone Mephistopheles knows.

But it is time to drink now. Mephistopheles takes Wagner's proffered glass, spits out the wine as rubbishy stuff, and calls on the figure of Bacchus sitting on the wine barrel (the sign of the inn) to supply something better. Magically, the little god obliges. Some sparkling wine spurts from the barrel, everyone fills his glass—and Mephistopheles proposes a toast to Marguerite.

This is too much for Valentine. He draws and challenges the stranger, who also draws and describes a circle on the ground about himself. As soon as the soldier steps inside the circle, his sword breaks in half.

Now the crowd knows with whom it has to deal. Led by Valentine, they sing the "Chorale of the Swords," in the middle of which they reverse their weapons, showing Mephistopheles the sign of the Cross in the handles. He cowers in fright before them—and stepping slowly backward to the impressive music, they leave him alone on the stage. It is a highly artificial, unrealistic scene, but invariably impressive.

When the male chorus, with its reversed swords, has left the stage, Mephistopheles regains his courage and mutters that he'll be glad to meet the crowd again. He then greets Faust, who comes in as the orchestra plays part of his aria in praise of passion and asks whether that vision of Marguerite he had seen was only a trick. No, says Mephistopheles, but adds— accompanied in the orchestra by a simple and hymnlike melody—that her own virtue and the protection of heaven may make her a difficult conquest.

No. 3
Andantino

With the rhythm of the coming waltz already in the orchestra, and the chorus returning to the stage, Mephistopheles tells Faust that he can meet her now, at the dance, which begins at once with the fiddles playing on open strings, as though tuning up. It is one of the most familiar melodies in this extremely familiar score, as it is a popular number for piano beginners and for band concerts; but its full effect is missed without the chorus, which sings a strongly marked tune of its own with a rhythm that crosses over the tune the orchestra plays (see p. 210). In most productions, the ballet does the dancing to the tune in the orchestra, while the chorus sways gently around it singing its own tune. Siebel stands on one side waiting for Marguerite and turns down invitations from some of the girls to join the dance; but just as our heroine is about to come on the stage, Mephistopheles frightens the youngster away—a bit of business that almost invariably gets a laugh.

For a moment the dance rhythms fade away as Marguerite comes on and Faust gallantly steps forward and offers to escort the beautiful young lady home. Gently, Marguerite denies her ladyship, her beauty, and any need for assistance (see p. 215).

She has sung only two lines (but very lovely ones), and Faust is passionately devoted to her, as he tells us in a few phrases that mount to a high B. Every tenor I have ever heard goes to the footlights for this high note and hurls it at the audience as loud as he can, even though it is marked *pianissimo* in the score.

The little break in the gay dancing scene makes a telling musical contrast, and it is cleverly managed dramatically, for the crowd stops to note it with the curiosity of all village gossips. Mephistopheles tells Faust he'll give him some lessons in wooing, while the crowd whispers that this is a most remarkable phenomenon—Marguerite's turning down so handsome a young stranger. But the desire to waltz mounts again with the music, our familiar tune comes back, and with the speeding up of the dance to a delirious tempo the scene ends.

Act Two

A BRIEF intermezzo before the second act suggests the mystery and calm of a summer night and, with an expressive clarinet solo over tremolo strings, the excitement of young love.

When the curtain goes up, the music changes to a fast tempo. The scene is the flowery garden of Marguerite's home, with the entrance to the house on the right, a door to the street in back, and, usually, a backdrop of a church. Siebel, in an agitated frame of mind, enters through the door, stops before the rosebush in the center of the stage, and begs the flowers to speak to Marguerite of the love he does not dare avow. It is the well-known "Flower Song" he sings (see p. 217), and at the end of the first stanza he picks a rose, which withers in his hand just as Mephistopheles had prophesied it would. (Actually, he just throws it away quickly.) There is a cure for

that, however. To the tune that accompanied Mephistopheles' reference to Marguerite's purity in the previous scene (No. 3), he dips his hand in a little bowl of water beneath a statue of the Virgin, where Marguerite prays every evening—and sure enough, the next flower he picks does not wither. (It does not occur to the simple-minded fellow that the Devil's promise about any flowers Siebel tries to pick has more than a literal meaning, that it refers to Marguerite's fate as well.) He repeats the "Flower Song," and dashes off to other parts of the garden to pick a bouquet just as Faust and Mephistopheles enter, with the orchestra playing the theme of Faust's desire for pleasure.

A moment later Siebel returns with a bouquet and leaves it triumphantly at Marguerite's door to a part of the "Flower Song" music. Mephistopheles ironically calls him a seducer as he leaves.

The Devil now tells Faust to wait here in the garden till he brings a gift that may turn out to be more persuasive than his rival's flowers, and Faust begins to feel the magic of the scene steal over him. He tells us so in the recitative that precedes the great tenor aria of this opera—"*Salut! demeure*"—a passionate paean to Marguerite's surroundings, the home that has made her so pure and lovable (see p. 220). A violin obbligato and a middle section that involves some surprising changes in key are among the features that have made it one of the two most popular tenor arias in French opera (the other being the "Flower Song" from *Carmen*). There is a high C toward the close that many tenors find difficulty in negotiating, and accordingly the aria is often transposed down a notch or two.

So deeply is Faust under the spell of the holy purity of this place that he has at least a moment's compunction about carrying out the planned seduction. When Mephistopheles returns, carrying a jewel box under his arm, Faust says he wants never to see Marguerite again; but the Devil merely laughs, places his rich present beside Siebel's bouquet, and takes his protégé off just before Marguerite comes in.

She is wondering aloud about the identity of the handsome young man with the noble air who talked to her at the kermesse, and at several points in the ballad "The King of Thule," which she sings at her spinning wheel, she stops to reconstruct the scene—how embarrassed she was, how she blushed, how like a *grand seigneur* he seemed.

Suddenly she espies the bouquet, which she recognizes at once as coming from Siebel, but beside it there is an ornate casket. At first she scarcely dares touch it—but there is a key, and, gathering her courage, she uses it. A vigorous tinkling from the triangle in the orchestra pit suggest the jewels she sees. She is transported with simple, childlike delight as she ornaments herself with these jewels and can scarcely believe that she is not really a *demoiselle*, as Faust had called her. Mephistopheles has thoughtfully included a mirror in the box so that she can get the full effect of his gift, and Marguerite's thoughts race between herself and the effect she might make on the handsome young stranger if he could only see her now. The music, of course, is the coloratura aria, the "Jewel Song" (see p. 226). It is a perfect expression of Marguerite's simple ecstasy but a stumbling block for sopranos who might sing the entire role competently if they did not have to master the trills and scales of this aria.

Martha, a middle-aged town gossip, now drops in. She assures Marguerite that the jewels must be the gift of a really highclass lover, and she is adding that her own husband has never been so generous, when Mephistopheles enters to ask with a deep bow for Lady Martha Schwerdtlein. That's Martha, of course, and he announces with mock gravity that her husband is dead and sends a greeting. As Martha performs a comic faint in the Devil's arms, Faust slips into the garden and begins complimenting Marguerite on how well she looks in her jewels.

The stage slowly darkens as night falls, and a masterly piece of dramatic composition ensues. On one side of the stage Mephistopheles with saturnine humor woos the eager Martha, telling her that hard circumstances make him a wanderer, poor fellow, and that he is an orphan who would like nothing better than to settle down comfortably. Martha eats all this up and throws out the most outrageously obvious hints that she would make him an excellent wife. All the time, the Devil keeps one eye on the two young lovers, whose relationship progresses tenderly. He allows them to wander to a distant part of the garden, marches Martha up and down the stage with great strides, and finally, in the darkness, gets rid of her. He steps behind the rosebush and invokes night to aid him in his designs on Marguerite's virtue. For a moment the bush glows with an evil reddish light, and then Mephistopheles disappears.

The famous love duet follows (see p. 232), a duet that may sound tame to ears educated on the sweaty ecstasies of the garden-scene love duet in *Tristan und Isolde*. And yet its variety of moods and the simple and touching depiction of a peasant girl falling romantically in love for the first time, make it one of the enduring glories of this opera. It begins with a faint protest from Marguerite that it is getting late, but Faust pleads that he wishes but to hold her hand a while. He sings a restrained but ardent melody, asking only to look at her beautiful face, a melody that Marguerite echoes, acknowledging the magic of the new feeling singing in her heart. A moment later she breaks away from him to pluck a flower and play the old game of he-loves-me-he-loves-me-not. The music becomes agitated and mounts to a triumphant he-loves-me as she pulls off the last petal. Now Faust presses his suit passionately. He does love her, and does she know what that avowal means? He will love her forever. Suddenly the music sinks to a single note in the horn; Faust and Marguerite embrace for their first kiss; and, their voices blending almost indistinguishably, they whisper the word "*éternelle*." It is a magical effect.

Overcome by emotion, Faust solemnly sings of the night of love surrounding them, and Marguerite replies with a direct avowal of her love-unto-death. In the orchestra, Marguerite's simple statement (Faust is incapable of any such sincerity) forms the bass part of her lover's address to the night, as though it is Marguerite's real love that forms the basis of Faust's emotion.

Suddenly Marguerite is panic-stricken by the strength of her own emotions. She begs Faust to leave and not to break her heart. He naturally protests; their voices rise in the exchange; but finally Faust's feeble better nature has a temporary triumph. With a cello playing the melody of "*Salut! demeure*," he tenderly promises to go, asking only to see her again the next day. "Yes, at dawn — tomorrow — always," answers Marguerite. She throws him one more kiss, and goes into the house.

But Mephistopheles has been watching this pretty scene. "Lunkhead!" he calls Faust as he stops him. "Stop a moment and listen to what she has to tell the stars."

Marguerite opens the window at this moment, looks out at the soft night, and pours out her heart: "What joy it is to be alive, to be in love! Tomorrow! Tomorrow! Come! Come!" With wood-wind obbligato, it is the most ecstatic moment in the opera.

He loves me! He loves me! What stirs in my heart?
Il m'ai-me! il m'ai-me! Quel trouble en mon coeur!

Faust is overwhelmed. He completely forgets his promise, and, with a shove from Mephistopheles, he rushes to the window and embraces Marguerite in a long, passionate kiss. Now

the full orchestra triumphantly swells out on the melody of the flute obbligato in No. 4 and then ebbs away to a pianissimo.

As the curtain slowly descends, Mephistopheles throws himself on a bench howling with laughter. He now believes he has both souls safe in his grasp.*

---

*Vladimir Rosing, the imaginative director of the American Opera Company, left no doubts in the minds of his audience over the progress of the rest of that night. He had Faust enter Marguerite's house; then Mephisto peeked in at the window, closed its shutters, and tiptoed away chuckling.

Act Three

THE brief scene which opens this act is omitted in modern productions; for while it has dramatic significance and its counterpart in Goethe, it is not strictly necessary for understanding the story, and part of the score is weak.

Marguerite has become the laughingstock of the other girls in the town, and she listens in her room to the cruel fun they make of her for having been deserted by her lover. Bitterly she reflects that once she used to make the same sort of fun of other girls in similar distress. Then, sitting at her spinning

wheel, she sings the aria *"Il ne revient pas"* ("He does not return"), known also as "The Spinning Wheel Song." It is not particularly effective.

Faithful Siebel tries to comfort her, but Marguerite only tells him that she still loves Faust. For the same English production which elicited "Even Bravest Heart May Swell" from Gounod, he wrote an extra aria for Siebel too, "When All Was Young." It was once a drawing-room favorite, but its sweet melody is seldom heard any more.

Act Three, Scene 1

WHEN producers omit the introductory scene just described, they must assume that their audiences are familiar enough with the story of *Faust* to know that some time has passed and that Marguerite is deserted. Their assumption appears to be justified, for the libretto is seldom accused of incoherence.

The deserted girl enters the church during a service and kneels apart from her neighbors to pray to God. Mephis-

topheles, at first invisible and later appearing out of an open tomb, mocks her attempts at prayer, and a chorus of demons off stage (all basses) calls menacingly to her. Mockingly, the Devil reminds her of her innocent past, and the church choir starts to sing the *Dies Irae*. Marguerite tries all the harder to pray; and with Mephistopheles telling her there is no pardon for her in heaven and the choir praying for forgiveness off

stage, Marguerite's voice rises higher and higher in her prayer. It reaches its climax; Mephistopheles pronounces a curse on her; and with a great shriek, Marguerite faints. The worshipers hear her at last, come crowding around, pick up her unconscious body, and the curtain descends to religious organ music.

Act Three, Scene 2

(NOTE: In the original score and in Goethe, the following scene comes before the previous one, lending even greater drama to Mephistopheles' appearance to Marguerite in the church and making it quite clear that she has by that time been deserted. The order given here, however, is the one generally followed today both in performance and in published scores.)

The soldiers who were ready to leave in the kermesse scene have now had their campaign and are returning—Valentine among them but with Wagner missing, as Mephisto had predicted. The "Soldiers' Chorus," which every American child has sung in school and which now seems so commonplace, was a stunner to the most sophisticated critics of 1859, and it still never fails of its effect on the stage. It starts very quietly in the orchestra, a clarinet playing the familiar melody. The soldiers then file on to the square between Marguerite's home and the church, and sing another tune to the same rhythm. In a brief colloquy between Valentine and Siebel (often omitted), the youngster tells the soldier that Marguerite is in the church. "Praying for me, no doubt," says Valentine. "What a time she'll have listening to my exploits!"

The stage band now comes on (if the opera company can afford one), and the "Soldiers' Chorus" proper is sung with loud crashes of cymbals, the ladies of the chorus silently but joyfully rushing in to welcome their men (see p. 236). At the end, the soldiers all step to the front of the stage, waving their swords on high. Then, to a jaunty little military tune, they file off, leaving the stage to Valentine and Siebel. Siebel is unequal to telling Valentine the truth about Marguerite, but he does arouse his suspicion that something is wrong by refusing an invitation to come in and have a drink. Terribly embarrassed, he gives equivocal answers to Valentine's questions and escapes into the church, while Valentine enters his own house to see what this is all about. Night begins to descend as Mephistopheles and Faust enter.

Just why or when Faust deserted Marguerite is made no clearer in the opera than it is in Goethe's play, but apparently the philosopher's conscience has been bothering him and he has insisted on returning. Mephistopheles has advised against what he regards as an incomprehensible and dangerous whim; but always obliging, according to the contract, he brings out a guitar and sings a mocking serenade to the girl (see p. 244). He points out that she is only feigning sleep, and actually is waiting for her lover's kiss, but he suggests she had better not give it to him before she has a wedding ring safe on her finger. At the close, Mephistopheles ranges over three whole octaves of demoniac *ha-has*—and Valentine bursts from the house in anger.

"What do you want?" he demands.

"Pardon," says Mephistopheles, "but the serenade wasn't intended for you." His sister heard it even better than he did himself, says Valentine, which is the first that Faust, who remains discreetly in the gackground, knows of the soldier's identity. In rage, Valentine runs his sword through Mephistopheles' guitar, but the Devil only politely inquires whether he doesn't have an ear for music.

That is all the persiflage Valentine will stand for. Which of the two, he challenges, is going to die for these insults to his honor? Faust feels obliged to take up the challenge; but in the trio that follows, he makes it clear that it goes against his conscience to draw the blood of Marguerite's brother. Simultaneously, in the melody that dominates this martial number, Valentine prays God to redouble his power and courage, while Mephistopheles comments with a grin that all this brave show isn't going to do the soldier any good. In the middle of the trio, while Mephistopheles gives some *sotto voce* advice to his protégé, Valentine tears a medallion from his neck—a gift from Marguerite which he had fondled affectionately while singing "Even Bravest Heart May Swell." He does not wish for protection from that source any longer, he cries, as he hurls it across the stage. Mephistopheles only says, "You'll be sorry."*

In the duel that follows, Mephistopheles at first acts as though he were referee, bringing his own sword up between the duelists' crossed ones. On the fourth exchange, however, he leaps to Faust's side, parries Valentine's weapon, and gives the opening by which Faust runs his adversary through. With a sardonic comment on the prostrate Valentine, Mephisto gathers up his cloak on the point of his sword and hurries Faust from the scene.

The neighbors, hearing the noise of the duel, rush out into the night and try to help the dying Valentine. The ominousness of the scene is well suggested by the persistent, regular beat in the bass of a low note, an organ point.

"Thanks," says Valentine to the two chorus men who try to hold him up, "but I have looked on death often enough not to be afraid of it"; and when Marguerite appears on the scene wringing her hands, he informs the whole neighborhood that he is dying on account of an idiotic fight with her lover. Painfully but with solemn anger, he turns on his sister and curses her out. "And should God pardon you at last," he ends, "be cursed here on earth."

The shallow crowd, which had expressed its own unflattering opinion of Marguerite in the previous act, thinks this is a bit too strong and won't do Valentine much good when it comes to making his own peace with heaven. It recoils with horror at the blasphemy, but Valentine only repeats his curse, accuses her of having murdered him, and with death already rattling in his throat, he says he dies a soldier.

The crowd is deeply impressed, sinks on its knees, and utters four bars of unaccompanied prayer for Valentine that is one of the most effective passages in the entire opera.

No. 5
Lento

May the good Lord take his soul and for give him his sin.
Que le Sei-gneur ait son âme et par-donne au pê-cheur.

The curtain descends on a soft but piercing theme reiterated three times by the wood winds.†

---

*Originally Gounod had composed a duet between Marguerite and Valentine in which she presents him with this protective medallion. It came near the beginning of the kermesse scene and was withdrawn to make a more effective entrance for Marguerite. The whole medallion business was an invention of the librettist's and does not appear in Goethe.

†The stage directions do not state specifically what Marguerite should do during the last bars of this scene, and various bits of more or less effective stage business have been devised for her. The most striking I ever saw was Geraldine Farrar's. She hovered for a moment over Valentine's body, then uttered a high, crazy wail totally unrelated to the music the orchestra was playing, and ran from the stage. She made it clear that Marguerite had already lost her mind.

Act Four

THE first part of this act is given at the Paris Opéra and for a few seasons about twenty-five years ago was also mounted at the Metropolitan Opera House. Today Americans seldom see it, and it forms no important part of the story.

Mephistopheles takes Faust first to the Walpurgis Night revels in the Harz Mountains, where ghosts frighten the philosopher. He then takes him to a more attractive spot where they join Cleopatra, Lais, and other antique queens of beauty in a banquet, and watch a ballet. The ballet music often forms a part of "pops" programs but is seldom danced today. Suddenly a theme from the love music comes in quietly, and then a vision of Marguerite appears in back. There is a line of blood about her neck, like the cut of an ax, cries Faust, and he demands to be taken to her at once. He rushes off, followed by Mephistopheles.

There is a short Prelude to the final scene, the only one in the last act generally to be given. The music before the raising of the curtain is based on three themes—the first two in minor suggesting the tragedy of Marguerite's plight:

and the third (based on Faust's aria in the garden scene) indicating Marguerite's innocence:

The curtain rises in the middle of the Prelude, an agitated passage in triplets suggesting the hurried ride of Faust and Mephisto to Marguerite's aid. The scene is her prison cell. Asleep in the dirty gray dress presumably supplied by the prison authorities, she lies on a pallet of straw on the floor. It is early morning, and Mephistopheles enters with Faust, tells him that if Marguerite is to be saved it must be done by mortal hands, leaves him the keys to the prison, tells him to hurry, and departs to watch outside.

In a brief soliloquy based on the three themes in the Prelude, Faust tells us what has brought Marguerite to this state. Gone literally mad after his desertion and her brother's death, she has killed their illegitimate child. Now she is to be hanged.

Marguerite, waking out of a horrible dream, hears him call to her*, throws her arms about him and cries that he has come to save her. Faust takes up the melody she sings, assuring her that nothing can part them now, not even Mephistopheles. But poor Marguerite's mind begins to wander. A single violin softly plays the melody of the kermesse waltz, and Marguerite imagines she is at the fair once more. She again is accosted by the handsome young stranger. And now she is in the garden, and again he is making love to her. Frightened by this elementary object lesson in psychiatry, Faust tries to urge her to come with him from the prison, but he cannot make her hear.

*Faust calls to Marguerite three times, his voice rising on the third syllable and falling on the last:

Mar-gue - ri - te!

At the end of the scene, after her delirious prayer, when Faust is less moved by remorse than by anxiety, his voice rises in great excitement on the second syllable:

Mar-gue -ri - te!

Now Mephistopheles bursts in, demanding that they hurry. His horses are waiting, and there is no telling what will happen if they delay longer. But Marguerite recognizes Mephistopheles. At first she shrinks away in fright; then she gets down on her knees and wildly prays to the angels of heaven to take her up into the light (see p. 248). Three times she repeats this prayer, each time a note higher than the last, while Faust and Mephistopheles urge her to come with them. Marguerite does not heed them, but looking at Faust, she thinks his hands are red with blood. "Go!" she cries, "you fill me with horror!" —and she falls over dead.

Mephistopheles is already gloating over the seizure of one more soul, when off stage a chorus of angels answers Mar-guerite's prayer. "She is saved!" they sing. "Christ is risen! Peace and happiness to all Christians!"

The theme of triumphant love (No. 4) once again is sung out by the full orchestra as a vision suggesting the apotheosis of Marguerite appears on the back wall of the prison. Solemnly, joyously, to the accompaniment of harps, an Easter hymn of forgiveness is sung.

And that is the end of the story of Marguerite. In many performances, Mephistopheles sweeps Faust out with him, as though to take him off straight to hell. There is no justification in the score for this sensible ending; and to see what really happened later on to this sinner, you will have to consult Part II of Goethe's *Faust*.

Kermesse

VIN OU BIÈRE

Allegretto
STUDENTS

Beer or__ bran - dy, Bran - dy or beer, We're__ not par -
Vin *ou__* *biè - re,* *Bière* *ou__* *vin,* *Que__* *mon__*

tic - u - lar, Bring it here! We've no pre - ju - dice, Glass for__
ver - re *Soit__* *plein!* *Sans* *ver - go - gne,* *Coup* *sur__*

WAGNER

glass We'll__ drink__ an - y - thing_____ you__ pass! Learn - ed__
coup, *Un__* *i - vro - gne_____* *Boit__* *tout!* *Jeune* *a -*

scholars at the wine-keg, Drink-ing wa-ter is a
dep - te Du ton - neau, N'en ex - cep - te Que

sin! Drink to glory, Drink to love, Get your
l'eau! Que ta gloi - re, Tes a - mours, Soient de

STUDENTS

glass and let's be-gin! Learn-ed schol-ars at the
boi - re Tou - jours! Jeune a - dep - te Du ton -

bar, Fly from wa-ter as a drink, Drink to
neau, N'en ex - cep - te Que l'eau! Que ta

glo - ry, Drink__ to__ love Come and let__ your__ glass - es
gloi - re, Tes__ a - mours, Soient de boi - re Tou -

clink!_____
jours!_____

p lightly

OLD MEN

All I ask is time on a Sun - day, Time for a joke,
Aux jours de di - manche et de fê - te, J'aime à par - ler

Even Bravest Heart

AVANT DE QUITTER

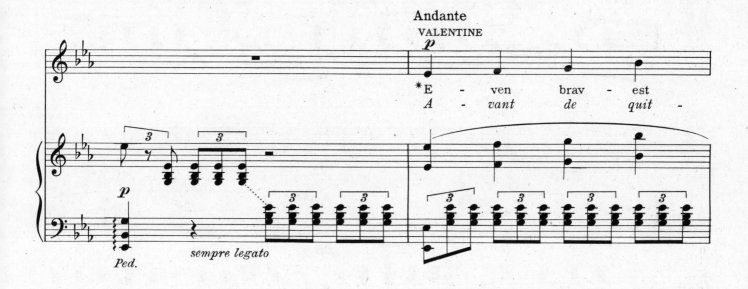

*This number was originally set to English words. The French translation is by O. Pradère.

pass - es round,   When a - lone _____ my _____
pro - té - ger,   Cet - te soeur _____ si ___ ché -

watch   I keep,   And my _____ com - rades
ri - - - e,   Dai - gne de tout dan -

lie _____ a - sleep, A - mong   their arms up - on the
ger _____ la pro - té - ger,   Dai - gne la pro - té -

tent - ed bat - tle - ground. _____
ger de tout dan - ger. _____

Waltz

Tempo di Waltz

CHORUS

As the wind that
Ain - si que la

whirls in the mead - ow
bri - se lé - gè - re
May gath - er from o - ver the
Sou - lève en é - pais tour - bil -

plain,
lons
Swirls of dust and drift - ing grain,
La pous - siè - re Des — sil - lons,

Swirls of dust and drift - ing grain.
La pous - siè - re Des - sil - lons,

So the
Que la

waltz sweeps up the danc - er, E - ven earth - bound
val - se nous en - trai - ne! Fai - tes re - ten -

feet must ans - wer To the mu - sic's gay re -
tir la plai - ne De l'é - clat de vos chan -

frain, to the mu - sic's gay re - frain.
sons, de l'é - clat de vos chan - sons!

SIEBEL

man to dance?_____ No, no!_____ No,
vi - te?_____ Non, non!_____ Non,

no!_____ I would tread on your feet!_____
non!_____ je ne veux pas val - ser!_____

CHORUS

As the wind that whirls in the mead - ow May
Ain - si que la bri - se lé - gè - re Sou -

gath - er from o - ver the plain, Swirls of dust and
lève en é - pais tour - bil - lons La pous - siè - re

) 213 (

drift - ing grain, Swirls of dust and drift - ing grain,
Des sil - lons, La pous - siè - re Des sil - lons,

So the waltz sweeps up the danc - er, E - ven
Que la val - se nous en - traî - ne! Fai - tes

earth - bound feet must ans - wer To the mu - sic's
re - ten - tir la plai - ne De l'é - clat de

gay - re - frain, to the mu - sic's gay re - frain.
vos chan - sons, De l'é - clat de vos chan - sons!

Pray, Do Not Think Me Bold

NE PERMETTREZ-VOUS PAS

Original key: G

Flower Song
LA FLEUR QUE TU M'AVAIS JETÉE

Original key: D-flat

Let your beau-ty re - mind her How much fair-er I find her,
Fleurs é - clo - ses près d'el - le, Di - tes - lui qu'elle est bel - le,

Let each pet - al de - clare _____ The love _____ I bear! _____
Que mon cœur nuit et jour _____ Lan - guit _____ d'a - mour! _____

_____ Let your blos-soms con - vey _____ What I _____ would say! _____
_____ Fai - tes - lui mes a - veux, _____ Por - tez _____ mes vœux! _____

L. H.

When she holds you be - fore her, Tell her how I a - dore her,
Ré - vé - lez à son â - me, Le se - cret de ma flam - me,

cresc.

That no flow-er can be as sweet as she!
Qu'il s'ex-hale a - vec vous Par - fums plus doux!

And it might not be a - miss,
Un bai - ser, un doux bai - ser,

While you're there, to steal a kiss!
Un bai - ser, un doux bai - ser!

Fair Home of Heaven's Fairest Angel

SALUT! DEMEURE

Larghetto

Fair home of heav-en's fair-est an-gel, Fair
Sa - lut! de-meu-re chaste et pu - re, Sa-

home of heav-en's fair-est an - gel! Ah, what de-light to know the
lut! de-meu-re chaste et pu - re, où se de-vi-ne la pré-

gar - den Where blows such a pure, per-fect blos - som!
sen - ce d'une âme in - no-cen-te et di - vi - ne!

What rich - es lie with - in this hum - ble place,
Que de ri - ches - se en cet - te pauv - re - té!

What hap-py dreams, what wealth of joy and grace!
En ce ré - duit, que de fé - li - ci - té!

What hid-den trea - sures,
Que de ri - ches - se,

what hid-den trea-sures lie with - in this place!
que de ri-ches-se en cet-te pauv-re - té!

What hap-py
En ce ré -

dreams, what wealth of joy and grace!
duit, que de fé - li - ci - té!

rit.   a tempo

pp   p

Fair home - 6

Here through the hours of dark - - ness,
Là que de ton ha - lei - - ne,

Heav'n sent its ra - diant star - - light, To
en - ve - lop - pant son â - - me, Tu

crown_____ a mor - tal maid, To form her like an
fis_____ a - vec a - mour é - pa - nou - ir la

an - gel sent down from the skies!_____ How
fem - me en cet an - ge des cieux!_____ C'est

blows such a blos - som! Fair home, _____ fair
cen - te et di - vi - ne! Sa - lut, _____ sa -

home of heaven's fair-est an - - - gel!
lut, de - meu-re chaste et pu - - - re,

Ah, what de - light to know the gar - den, where dwells such a maid - en, such an
où se de - vi - ne La pré - sen - ce d'une âme in - no - cen - te et di -

rit. molto
Adagio

an - - gel!
vi - - ne!

Tempo I

Jewel Song

AH! JE RIS DE ME VOIR

Ah,   I see_____ beau-ty that is smil-ing back to me.
Ah,   je ris_____ de me voir Si belle en ce mi-roir.

Is   it   true,_____   Mar - ga - ri - ta,
Est - ce   toi,_____   Mar - gue - ri - te,

Is it you?   An-swer me,   can it be,   can it be that I am
Est - ce toi?   Ré-ponds-moi,   ré-ponds-moi,   ré-ponds, ré-ponds, ré-ponds,

dream - ing?   No,   No,   what can this
vi - te!   Non!   non!   ce n'est plus

What can this mean, What can this mean?
Ce n'est plus toi, Ce n'est plus toi,

You are dressed like a queen, Hail to queen Mar - gue -
C'est la fil - le d'un roi, Qu'on sa - lue au pas -

ri - te!
sa - ge!

Ah, could he look at me,
Ah, s'il é - tait i - ci!

Dressed as I want to be,
S'il me vo - yait ain - si!

Now if I could be near him,
Com - me u - ne de - moi - sel - le

Now I would wait to hear him, Ah! _____
Il me trou - ve - rait bel - le, Ah! _____

_____ And one so high a - bove me might be - gin to
_____ *Com - me u - ne de - moi - selle Il me trou - ve - rait*

love me, And one so high a - bove me might be - gin to
bel - le, Com - me u - ne de - moi - selle Il me trou - ve - rait

love ____ me! Mar - gue - ri - te,
bel - le! Mar - gue - ri - te,

What can this mean?   Whose   the   im - age be -
Ce   n'est plus toi,   *Ce   n'est plus ton vi -*

fore_____ you,   Ah!   You're as fair as a
sa   - - ge!   *Non!   C'est la fil - le d'un*

queen,_____   And your king would a -
roi,_____   Qu'on sa - lue au pas -

dore_____ you!
sa - - - - - - - - - - - ge!

Love Duet

LAISSE-MOI

Original key: F

Stay, my dear,__ stay and hear
Lais - se - moi,__ lais - se - moi

what my heart has to tell you, How I feel the en-
con - tem - pler ton vi - sa - ge, Lais - se - moi con - tem -

chant - ment of your love - - ly eyes.
pler___ ton vi - sa - - - ge!

Now the pale eve-ning star,___ Peers through the
*Sous la pâ - - le clar - té*___ *Dont l'as - tre*

dark-'ning skies,___ Striv-ing vain-ly to ex-cel you, And
*de la nuit*___ *Com-me dans___ un nu - a - ge,* *Ca-*

fail - ing, must wor-ship from a-far!
res - se, *ca - res - se ta beau - té!*

Adagio

FAUST
MARGUERITE

Night of rap-ture! Night of rap-ture!
É - ter - nel - le! *É - ter - nel - le!*

live to a - dore you, To live and die for
tiens! je t'a - do - re! Pour toi je veux mou -

you!___ Love me,
rir!___ Par - le,

I im - plore you, Ah! I a -
parle en - co - re! Ah! je t'a -

dore you! Ah let me live and die, yes, live and die for you!___
do - re! Pour toi je veux mou-rir, pour toi je veux mou-rir!___

Soldiers' Chorus

GLOIRE IMMORTELLE

March time
CHORUS

Original key: B-flat

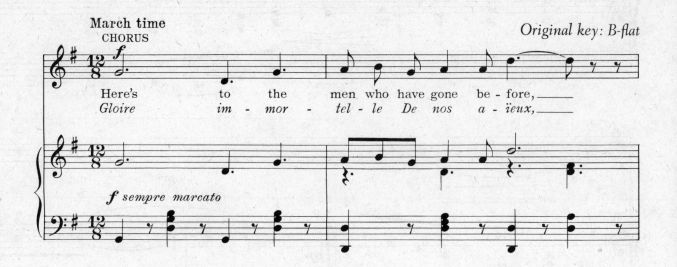

Here's to the men who have gone be - fore,_____
Gloire im - mor - tel - le De nos a - ïeux,_____

He - roes of man - y an an - cient war!_____
Sois nous fi - dè - le, mou - rons comme eux!_____

Glo - ry and hon - or be their re - ward,_____ And
Et sous ton ai - le, Sol - dats vain - queurs,_____ Di -

have at her call what-ev-er be-fall, The sword___ of the son!___
fer à la main, le fer à la main cou- rez___ aux com-bats!

legato
dim.

pp

Here's to the men who have gone be-fore,___
Gloire im - mor - tel - le De nos a - ïeux,___

pp

cresc.

He - roes of man-y an an-cient war!___
Sois nous fi - dè - le, mou-rons comme eux!___

cresc.
cresc.

Glo - ry and hon-or be their re - ward.___ And
Et sous ton ai - le, Sol - dats vain - queurs,___ Di -

laugh - ter of the girls we love so well,_____
pas, vers nos fo - yers hâ - tons le pas._____

Now_____ this ver - y night_____ we'll know the
No - - - tre pa - ys_____ nous tend les

com - fort of the homes that we de - fend - ed,_____ The brav - est
bras, L'a - mour nous rit, l'a - mour nous fê - te,_____ Et plus d'un

heart_____ will quake with fear,_____ The brav - est
cœur_____ fré - mit tout bas,_____ fré - mit tout

day, We're on our way with-out de - lay._____
pas, Hâ - tons le pas, Ne tar - dons pas._____

ff

Here's to the men who have gone be - fore,_____
*Gloire im - mor - tel - le De nos a - ïeux,*_____

He - roes of man - y an an - cient war!_____
*Sois nous fi - dè - le, mou - rons comme eux!*_____

Glo - ry and hon - or be their re - ward,_____ And
*Et sous ton ai - le, Sol - dats vain - queurs,*_____ *Di -*

may they im - part Their cour - age of heart! And may they im -
ri - ge nos pas, en - flam - me nos cœurs! Di - ri - ge nos

part____ Their cour - age of heart! And may they im -
pas,____ en - flam - me nos cœurs! Di - ri - ge nos

part_____ Their cour - age of heart,____ Their
pas,_____ di - ri - ge nos pas,____ en -

rit.

cour - age of heart!____
flam - me nos cœurs!____

sf

Mephisto's Serenade
VOUS QUI FAITES L'ENDORMIE

Original key

Allegretto

MEPHISTOPHELES

Don't pre - tend that you are sleep - ing On your
Vous qui fai - tes l'en - dor - mi - e, N'en - ten -

Bet - ter be a - fraid! Ha, ha, ha,
Et ton cœur l'en croit. Ah, ah, ah,

ha, ha, ha, ha, ha, ha, ha!
ah, ah, ah, ah, ah, ah, ah!

Lock your doors and win - dows tight - ly
N'ou - vre ta por - te, ma bel - le,

While you're still a maid, Bar
Que la bague au doigt, N'ou -

your doors and win-dows tight-ly, Bet-ter be a-
vre ta por-te, ma bel-le, Que la bague au

fraid While you're still a maid; Ha, ha, ha,
doigt, Que la bague au doigt. Ah, ah, ah,

ha, ha, ha, ha, ha, ha, ha! Ha, ha, ha, ha!
ah, ah, ah, ah, ah, ah, ah! ah, ah, ah, ah!

Presto

Final Trio

ANGES PURS

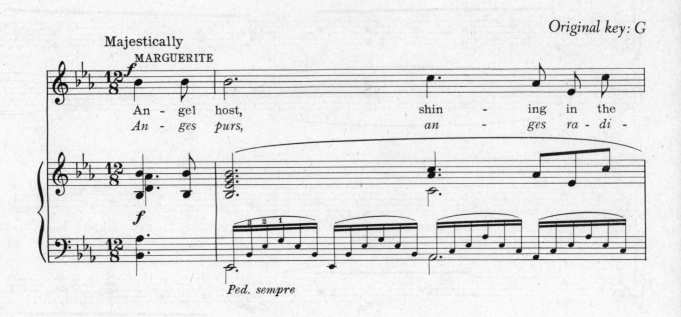

Majestically

MARGUERITE

An - gel host, shin - ing in the
An - ges purs, an - ges ra - di-

Ped. sempre

sky,_____ Lift up my soul to God on
eux,_____ Por-tez mon âme au sein des

high!_____ Kind heav - en, Let my sin be for -
cieux!_____ Dieu jus - te, à toi je m'a-ban-

giv - - en,   O God,   pit - y a soul _____ un -
don - - ne!   Dieu bon,   je suis à toi, _____ par-

shriv - - en!   An - gel host,   shin - ing in the
don - - ne!   An - ges purs,   an - ges ra - di -

sky, _____   Lift up my soul _____ to God _____ on
eux, _____   Por - tez mon âme _____ au sein _____ des

heav - en, let my sin be for - giv - - en! O
jus - te, à toi je m'a-ban - don - - ne! Dieu

Come _____ it's I! _____
Viens! _____ suis - moi! _____

MEPHISTOPHELES

It is morn - ing,
L'heu-re son - ne!

heav - en, let my sin be for - giv - - en! Mer - ci - ful
jus - te, à toi je m'a-ban - don - - ne! je suis à

Come _____ it's I! _____ Oh,
Viens _____ suis - moi! _____ suis -

Shadows de-part, and _ the
Dé - jà le jour en - va -

) 251 (

God,_____ I cry_____ to heav - - en! An - gel
toi,_____ Dieu bon,_____ par - don - - ne! An - ges

come,_____ come_____ let us fly!
moi,_____ viens_____ je le veux!

day, and__ the day is nigh!_____
hit, en - va - hit les cieux!

host, shin - ing in the sky,_____ Lift up my
purs, an - ges ra - di - eux,_____ Por- tez mon

Come, come_____ let__ us fly,_____ Shadows de-
Viens, viens! quit-tons ces lieux,_____ Dé - jà le

Come a - way, come a - way!_____ It is time__ to fly, Shadows de-
Hâ - tons-nous, Hâ - tons - nous_____ de quit- ter__ ces lieux, Dé - jà le

soul   to   God   on   high!_____   Kind   heav-en,
âme   au   sein   des   cieux!_____   Dieu   jus - te,

part   and   the day   is   nigh._____   Come,
jour   en - va-hit   les   cieux!_____   Viens!_____

part   and   the day   is   nigh._____   Come a -
jour   en - va-hit   les   cieux!_____   Suis nos

May a   sin-ner im - plore   you!   To hear   one — who kneels   be -
à   toi je m'a-ban-don - - ne!   Dieu bon,   je suis à   toi,   par -

come,_____   it's   I,_____   it's   I   pleading be -
viens!_____   C'est   moi,____   c'est moi   qui te l'or -

way!____   Come a - way!____   Come! __   Free - dom is be -
pas,____   suis nos   pas,____   Viens, __   ou   je t'a-ban-

fore you. An - gel host, shin - ing in the sky,_____
don - ne! An - ges purs, an - ges ra - di - eux!_____

fore you, Come, come morning is nigh,_____
don - ne. Viens, viens! quit-tons ces lieux!_____

fore you! Come a - way! Come a - way!_____ it is time_ to
don - ne! Hâ-tons-nous hâ-tons-nous_____ de quit-ter_ ces

Lift up my heart_____ to God_____ on high!__
Por - tez mon âme_____ au sein_____ des cieux!__

Shadows de - part_____ and the day_____ is nigh!__
Dé - jà le jour_____ en - va - hit_____ les cieux!__

fly! Shadows de - part_____ and the day_____ is nigh!__
lieux! Dé - jà le jour_____ en - va - hit_____ les cieux!__

rall.

) 254 (

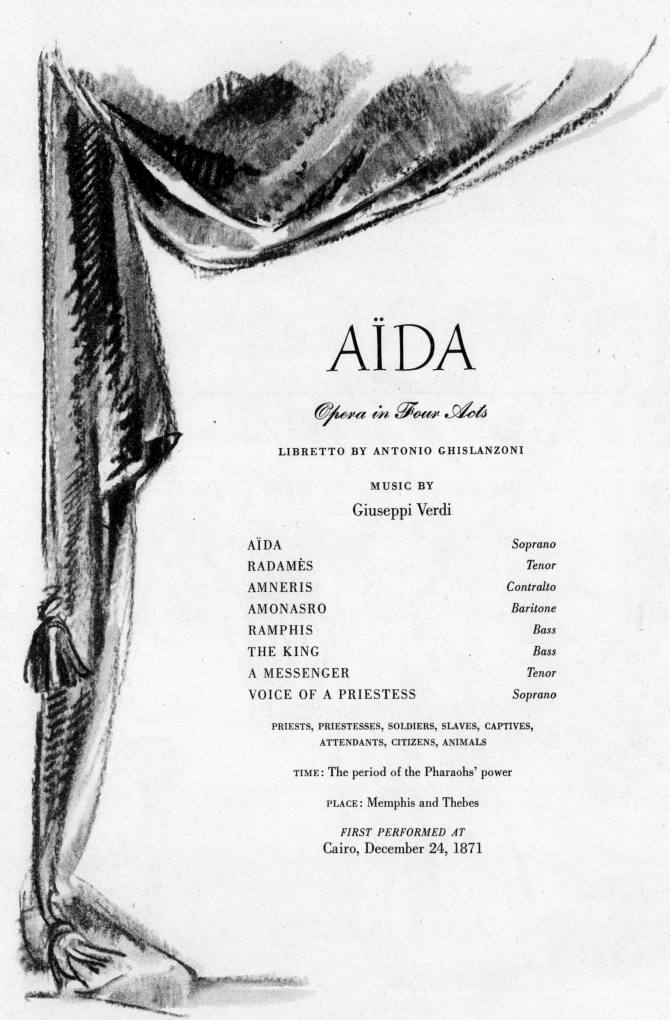

AÏDA

Opera in Four Acts

LIBRETTO BY ANTONIO GHISLANZONI

MUSIC BY

Giuseppi Verdi

AÏDA	*Soprano*
RADAMÈS	*Tenor*
AMNERIS	*Contralto*
AMONASRO	*Baritone*
RAMPHIS	*Bass*
THE KING	*Bass*
A MESSENGER	*Tenor*
VOICE OF A PRIESTESS	*Soprano*

PRIESTS, PRIESTESSES, SOLDIERS, SLAVES, CAPTIVES,
ATTENDANTS, CITIZENS, ANIMALS

TIME: The period of the Pharaohs' power

PLACE: Memphis and Thebes

FIRST PERFORMED AT
Cairo, December 24, 1871

Aïda

GIUSEPPE VERDI

IN HIS art, as in his life, Giuseppe Verdi exemplifies a profound integrity. That integrity is well illustrated by the story of the writing and production of *Aïda*.

In 1869 both the Suez Canal and the theater at Cairo were opened. Ismail Pasha, the Khedive of Egypt, wanted an important new work to honor his metropolis, which now, he knew, would rapidly grow in size and importance.* Verdi was asked and refused. He did not need the large fee offered, and he knew of no subject to tempt him. Finally a French friend, Camille du Locle, sent him the printed outline of a story with the assurance that it had been written by "a powerful personage." Verdi was honest enough to become enthusiastic over the possibilities of the outline, even though he thought he was being deceived by the "powerful personage" part of Du Locle's letter. Actually, the story did come from the distinguished Auguste-Edouard Mariette, a French Egyptologist whose work had so pleased the Khedive that he gave him the title of Bey or Pasha and Inspector General of Monuments. One of Mariette's services to the Khedive was digging out from his researches the incident in Egyptian history on which *Aïda* is based. He did not specify the date of the incident any more closely than the time of the Pharaohs. This, according to Mariette's own guesses, could be any time between 5004 B.C. and A.D. 381.†

Verdi, after consulting with his worldly-wise ex-pupil Angelo Mariani, asked for the equivalent of $20,000 for the score and $30,000 if he came himself to supervise the *première*. The offer was accepted by wire within three days. Du Locle, whose work on the French adaptation of *La Forza del Destino* Verdi had admired, made a French libretto out of Mariette's outline, and then Verdi, through his publisher Ricordi but at his own expense, engaged Antonio Ghislanzoni to prepare the final Italian version.

This Ghislanzoni was a versatile fellow. He was not only a librettist, but a novelist, a physician, a double-bass player, and an operatic baritone as well. He had helped with revisions of Verdi's *La Forza del Destino* and *Don Carlos,* and he wrote the books for two other operas produced the same year as *Aïda*—Cagnoni's *Papà Martin* and Braga's *Reginella*. Part of the time he worked at Verdi's estate in Sant' Agata, but a sizable correspondence between the composer and librettist still exists, and from this it is quite clear that Verdi was his own dramatist and Ghislanzoni a mere versifier. Verdi would write and say that he wanted verses of so many syllables per line with accents at certain places, when Aïda should be saying this or that and Amneris that or this. Sometimes Ghislanzoni's lines would not quite come up to specifications, and Verdi would write complimenting him on how beautiful they were, but— and he would suggest changes. For the last scene of the opera, Verdi sent Ghislanzoni his own idea of what the verses should be like and then proceeded to set them to music before he got his librettist's version. The final version is a compromise, worked out at Sant' Agata.

For a first payment Verdi received 50,000 francs. Shortly before, Paris had fallen to the Germans, and Verdi, who hated and feared the growing power of Germany, instructed Du Locle, his agent, to distribute 2000 francs "where you think they will do the most good to succor your poor, brave, wounded soldiers. With the remaining forty-eight thousand, buy me Italian bonds."

When it came time to produce *Aïda*, Verdi did not want to go to Cairo, for he never liked to travel. Instead, he made his own choice of a conductor, Giovanni Bottesini, and paid his salary. At the same time, he wrote to the regular conductor at the Cairo theater that he had the highest regard for him, but he would under-

---

*It is highly improbable that it was hoped to open the theater with a new opera, as has long been said and was repeated as recently as 1942 by Franz Werfel in his edition of Verdi's letters. In 1869, the year of the opening of both theater and canal, it was not yet determined who would be asked to compose the opera, Wagner or Verdi. At any rate, it was not till two years later that the opera was completed and produced.

†This long stretch makes one marvel at the temerity of critics who question the "historical accuracy" of the costumes or dances of any given performance. It does seem safe to assume, however, that the instruments used by the Theban Brass Band in the Triumphal March were not discovered in Mariette's researches.

stand how important it was that someone who had worked directly with the composer should have charge. He also insisted on—and got—several changes in the originally proposed cast.

Just before the opening, the critic Filippo Filippi wrote to Verdi telling him that he was going to Cairo for the sole purpose of reviewing the performance. The answer Verdi wrote to Filippi is a model of simple, honest tact. He told the critic, in effect, that he thought most highly of him, but he wished he would stay home. Publicity is no help to art, he said, and he pined for the old days when his works stood or fell simply on their own merits. Nevertheless, Filippi went; but he confined most of his review to a condescending and snobbish description of the colorful audience.

The opening had to be delayed some months on account of the Franco-Prussian War, which kept both Mariette and the scenery locked up in Paris. According to the contract Verdi had carefully made, he would be allowed to produce the opera elsewhere immediately after the date originally set for its Egyptian *première*. When he first learned of the delay (but not of its cause) he was characteristically set upon giving the *première* to Milan; but when he learned that the delay was no fault of the Egyptians but rather of the war, he readily gave up his legal right. The *première* finally took place in Cairo on Christmas Eve, 1871. The opera was an enormous success from the first and has, of course, remained one ever since in every country. It is a favorite for opening nights, and here is a list of a few of the great artists who made their debuts at the Metropolitan Opera House in this work: Toscanini (who also made his debut as a conductor at the age of nineteen leading a performance of *Aïda* in South America without a score and at a few hours' notice), Destinn, Onegin, Castagna, Giannini, Wettergren, Roman, Journet, Jagel and Moscona.

The story is not a subtle one. With the possible exception of Amneris, the characters are two-dimensional figures, and one of them—the King—is scarcely one-dimensional. Yet, it is probably the very simplicity of the character-drawing that made Verdi see the possibilities in the story and that has contributed in part to the great success this opera has had. Never for a moment is there any question about what is happening on the stage—not even for those who do not know the language and have not bothered to read about the opera. In a work so full of pageantry and large ensemble numbers, this is a rare virtue. Compare *Aïda* with, say,

Boris Godunov, in this respect, and the merits of its libretto become very clear. As a psychological study and as socially significant drama, *Boris* is infinitely superior to *Aïda* (and to practically every other opera ever performed); but as a clear story that anyone can understand, *Aïda* has few rivals. It also gave Verdi opportunity after opportunity for dramatic contrasts in music and in the representation of powerful emotions. He met every challenge magnificently.

As sheer storytelling, there are a few minor blemishes in the libretto. For instance, it is never made clear how Amonasro, the one Ethiopian warrior to be kept in chains, could meet Aïda at night alone on the Nile. Furthermore, he had apparently been in close touch with a new military power fresh from Ethiopia. Nor is it made clear how Aïda managed to get into the crypt to die with her lover.*

La Traviata, the other Verdian opera represented in this volume, has, of course, a more subtle and more moving book. But musically, *Aïda* is far more colorful and complex. *Aïda* was produced eighteen years after *La Traviata,* and it retains the freshness of melody and the power of dramatic conviction that mark Verdi's earlier works. In addition, it has a richness and ingenuity of orchestration that he never before had achieved. Part of this new richness—but only part—lies in the musical local color that Verdi has given his Egyptian story. The most casual listener can hear this in the song of the priestess (see p. 281), in the opening of the Nile scene, and even in the Triumphal March (see p. 285). In addition, Verdi had made great advances in his balancing of the string, wood-wind, and brass choirs of the orchestra.

But the musical advance does not lie merely in the orchestral coloring. It lies also in the greater rhythmic, harmonic and melodic variety and the surer marriage of these musical elements to the dramatic elements. Compare, for instance, the great ensemble numbers in the second and third acts of *Aïda* and *La Traviata* respectively. Effective and full of fine melody as is

---

*The latter point was clear enough in Verdi's own version of the last act. Here is one of Aïda's speeches, expunged after consultation with Ghislanzoni:

> *My heart knew your sentence.*
> *For three days I have waited here.*

This should clear up the matter for Giovanni Martinelli (once the best of the Metropolitan's Radamès), who was asked on a musical quiz program what it is that Aïda dies of. "No one exactly knows," replied the Metropolitan's leading Radamès. Had these lines been retained, the trancelike words and music of the heroine contrasted with the practical efforts of the hero—as well as her death in his arms before he feels so much as discomfort from the closeness of the air—would have had more dramatic clarity.

the latter, it has little of the strong contrasts that show conflicting emotions in the *Aïda* climax. The counterpoint in *Aïda* is far richer, too, and it does not depend on the basic hurdy-gurdy waltz rhythm that makes *La Traviata* sound naïve to some ears. Or consider the brief quotations of the themes (given in the following pages) associated with Aïda, with the priests, with Amneris, and note how musically just they are for the characters they depict.

It was such developments as these in the art of Verdi that prompted critics of the 1870's and later to accuse him of being influenced by Wagner. The accusation made him bitter. It spoiled for him the enormous triumph that *Aïda* achieved from the very first. For the great Italian, who, approaching sixty, was the acknowledged master of Italian opera, was made to feel that people thought he had learned from the rising German master. Verdi respected Wagner, but he never imitated him.

Stated in perhaps over-simplified extremes, there was this fundamental difference between the two composers: the Italian regarded opera as something that is sung with an orchestral accompaniment, while the German regarded "music drama" as orchestral composition with voices playing an important part in it. The development of Verdi's art must have seemed quite honestly to the early critics to be deeply influenced by Wagner, both in the respects already mentioned and in others—particularly in the greater flow of the music, the soft-pedaling of set numbers in the interest of carrying on the drama in one straight line. Today, tracing the development of Verdi from the early operas, through *Aïda* and beyond, to *Otello* and *Falstaff*, we can see more easily that it is all one clear, logical development and that Wagnerism, however generously he spoke of it, was foreign to his concept of what opera really should be.

The ultimate triumphs of Verdi's art, *Otello* and *Falstaff*, are the works most deeply admired by professional musicians. But it is *Aïda* which has won the greatest general popularity. It is, in fact, the most frequently performed opera in all the standard repertoire.

Prelude

THE Prelude to *Aïda* begins softly in the violins with the theme usually played when Aïda herself enters.*

No. 1
Andante

It is developed briefly and contrapuntally when the cellos interrupt with the ominous, magisterial theme associated with Aïda's unwitting enemies, the priests of Isis:

*But by no means always, as those who insist on Wagner's influence on Verdi would have us believe. Several times Aïda enters without this theme (it is, for example, not used at all in the final scene), and Aïda herself sings the theme both in the great first-act aria *("Ritorna vincitor!")* and in the second, when Amneris falsely reports the death of Radamès.

No. 2
Andante

Now the two themes are quickly developed to a loud climax, when once more Aïda's theme comes in softly by itself, has another quick development, and leads to a still more powerful climax. After this the Prelude fades to a quiet ending. In the last three bars, the violins climb way up—*ppp*—just as they do at the close of the opera. In this way the conflict between Aïda's love and the implacability of the priests—a conflict that ends with Aïda's seeing the gates of heaven open before her—is suggested even before the curtain goes up.

Act One, Scene 1

THE opening scene, usually with a shallow setting so that not too much time is lost in shifting to the more elaborate second scene, is the hall of the palace of a King of Memphis. His name and exact date are deliberately not given: it is enough to know that the story takes place some time during the reign of the Pharaohs. In back is a large gate, and the backdrop immediately tells the audience where the action takes place, for it is painted with pyramids and Egyptian palaces and temples. To the right (or, in some sets, the left), there are colonnades and the entrance to the temple of Isis. Ramphis, the high priest, is talking in solemn tones to Radamès, a young officer. He tells him that a messenger is expected shortly to confirm the report that the Ethiopians are again attacking Thebes and the valley of the Nile. Isis, adds Ramphis, looking without too much subtlety at Radamès, has already chosen the young and mighty soldier who is to lead the Egyptians in battle; but now he must make his report to the King.

He goes, and Radamès has his one great aria in the opera—*"Celeste Aïda"** (see p. 269). In the recitative, Radamès hopes that he may be the chosen battle leader, that he may return in triumph to Memphis, and that he may then tell Aïda that it was she for whom he fought and conquered. The aria itself describes the beauty of the heroine in conventionally heroic terms and ends with the wish that Radamès may be able to

*Coming this early, the aria is a cruel and unfair test for the leading tenor. Not only does it come before he has had a chance to warm up (he has only four bars of music in the colloquy with Ramphis), but latecomers are still being seated in the auditorium. Many a tenor has been damned for the way he sang this one overfamiliar aria, even though he may have done exceptionally well the rest of the evening. Perhaps to get even with the composer for putting the aria so early in the show, tenors always shout the concluding high B flat instead of fading away on it to an almost inaudible tone—the more appropriate idea Verdi had for the dreamy text.

return Aïda to her own country and there build a throne for her near the sun itself.

For Aïda is an Ethiopian and the personal servant of the Princess Amneris, daughter of the King. Aïda is supposed to be black as any full-blooded Ethiopian, but many prima donnas compromise in their make-up with a light sunburn effect. What neither Radamès nor any other Egyptian knows at this point of the story is that Amneris' slave is also a princess, being the daughter of Amonasro, King of the Ethiopians.

The duet and trio that follow this aria are full of nineteenth-century dramatic asides, but the conflicting emotions made clear by this old-fashioned device are powerfully underlined in the music. A melody which, with its slow triplets, manages to suggest both a regal bearing and the intense femininity of the Princess, announces the entrance of Amneris:

No. 3
Allegro assai moderato

She comes on the stage while Radamès is still lost in his daydream, and remarks on the joy that seems to transfigure his face. Then—in what is virtually an unashamed declaration of love—she says to him that the woman who could call up such joy would certainly be an enviable person. Radamès assigns the emotion to the hope he has of being chosen general, but Amneris persists: "Isn't there some gentler desire that you have—right here in Memphis?" His look tells her that if there is such a gentler desire, its cause is not Amneris; and in a couple of simultaneous asides, she indicates that she understands that look while he expresses the fear that he has given away his feelings for Aïda.

The orchestra plays the gentle theme of Aïda herself (No. 1), and the slave enters. Amneris immediately senses who her rival is and tells us so in an aside. She turns at once to Aïda to welcome her—not as a slave, she says, or as a servant, but as a sister. If Aïda is weeping—as she is now—she must tell Amneris why.

Aïda says it is the prospect of war with her native country that makes her weep; but Amneris sees through her just as easily as she had seen through Radamès, while they, in turn, immediately sense her suspicions. The suspicions of all three are indicated throughout by an agitated theme in the orchestra, most frequently associated with the jealousy of Amneris:

No. 4
Allegro agitato

The situation is one of those possible only in opera: the three principals are strung thinly across the stage, each simultaneously expressing his emotions; and the blend of the three voices unifies the conflict into a single strong effect.

A fanfare now announces the entrance of Ramphis, the King, and a large portion of the army and the priesthood. They are called together, says the King, to hear the fateful news from a messenger who has just arrived from Ethiopia. The messenger comes dashing in and, in an excited recitative, accompanied by low tremolos in the strings, reports that the Ethiopians have invaded Egypt and laid waste the crops; that Thebes is already resisting the invader; and that the Ethiopians are led by a fierce, indomitable warrior named Amonasro. Everyone recognizes this name: it is the King of Ethio-

pia's; and (in an aside) Aïda murmurs that it is her father. In a short, excited chorus, the men call for battle.

The King now announces what we had already suspected: the Goddess Isis has chosen Egypt's generalissimo—Radamès; and he orders the young man to go at once to the temple of Vulcan, god of weapons, to be armed for holy battle. Then the King begins the first of *Aïda's* magnificent choral ensemble numbers, a solemn, marchlike tune, calling on the Egyptians to defend the sacred Nile (see p. 275). Ramphis, the priests, and the other men all join in; Amneris takes a standard and proudly presents it to Radamès; while Aïda stands to one side and, her voice soaring above all the rest, gives vent to her conflicting emotions. Whom is she to pray for? Her own countrymen? Or the man she loves, who is about to go to fight them? The music works up to a series of shouts for battle (*"Guerra! guerra! guerra!"*), and then Amneris turns once more to Radamès and triumphantly sings *"Ritorna vincitor!"* (*"Return as conqueror!"*).

No. 5
Allegro

Re - turn   as con - quer - or!
Ri - tor - na vin - ci - tor!

The chorus repeats this in a higher key, and everyone marches off to the majestic measures of the King's call to battle.

That is, all but Aïda. With a kind of dramatic irony, she repeats Amneris' *"Ritorna vincitor!"* and, in a long, difficult aria, in which one magnificently appropriate melody follows another, she prays first for the safety of her father, then recalls what his triumph would mean to Radamès, and ends with a pitiful, heartfelt prayer to the gods to have pity on her (see p. 277). It is one of the greatest arias—or *scenas*—in operatic literature; and the bows at the end of the scene are usually reserved for the soprano who sings it.*

Act One, Scene 2

THE solemn second scene advances the story in no way at all, but the opera would be greatly the loser without it. In the deep, dimly lit temple of Vulcan,† with pillars stretching back into invisible distance, a high altar in the middle, statues of various deities on the side, and golden tripods with incense smoking—all of it lit with a dim, religious light—the priests are gathered for the ceremony. Off stage the chorus of priestesses, led by a single soprano accompanied by harps, sings

the beginning of the prayer supposed to be modeled on ancient Eastern melodic intervals (see p. 281):

No. 6
Andante

The male voices on stage come in with a soft, unaccompanied chant—and then the solemn dance of the priestesses before the altar takes place. During it, Radamès comes in,

---

†Vulcan was, of course, the Roman god of fire, a highly improbable Egyptian deity. But Verdi's librettists and audiences have always been broad-minded in such matters.

---

* The arrangement of this aria given on pages 277 to 280 includes only a part of the second, more smoothly melodic, half.

unarmed, and before the altar a silver veil is placed over his head. Ramphis presents him with an anointed sword and then prays to the gods for the protection of Egypt's sacred soil:

Radamès and the chorus take up this melody; the off-stage chorus of priestesses repeats the harp-accompanied prayer (No. 6), while on stage No. 7 is developed to a great climax. The music fades away again over the harp accompaniment, and the ceremony ends with a brief invocation to Phthà.

No. 7
Andante cantabile

Great God and great a - veng-ing power Guard of this ho - ly coun - try,
Nu - me, cu-sto-de e vin - di - ce di quest-a sa - cra ter - ra,

Grant us this sa-cred bless - ing, Bless-ings, blessings on E - gypt land!
la ma-no tua di - sten - di so - vra, so-vra l'e - gi - zio suol.

Act Two, Scene 1

THE first scene of Act II is laid, according to the score, in "a hall in the apartments of Amneris," though customarily today it has the outdoor setting of a terrace. The Princess reclines voluptuously on a couch while female slaves get her ready for the ceremonies of triumph that are scheduled for the victorious return of Radamès and his army. The women sing the praise of the triumphant warrior—in gentle rather than martial strains—and add that their songs are also about love. At the conclusion of each of the three stanzas, Amneris sings a slow, expressive, descending phrase, like a great sigh of impatient love. The proceedings are interrupted at one point by a quick, light dance of the Moorish slaves, whose eccentric movements almost always delight the audience.

The cellos play the theme associated with Aïda (No. 1), and as she approaches, Amneris dismisses all the rest. Aïda's sorrow, she tells them, is sacred to her, but in an aside we learn that now she means to find out whether her suspicions about Aïda's love are well founded.

Amneris greets her handmaiden compassionately, promising anything she wants to ease the sorrow she must feel. Nothing, says Aïda, can make her happy so far from her native land, ignorant of her father's and brothers' fate. Still, suggests Amneris, time may heal that sorrow should she fall in love. The suggestion has the expected effect. In an aside, to the melody of No. 1, Aïda sings of her love, while Amneris, seeing the force of the emotion she has aroused, is surer than ever that she is on the right track.

Now, to an appropriately insinuating melody of too-cloying sweetness, the Princess invites her slave to confide in her:

No. 8
Moderato

Then she goes on to report that Radamès has been killed by the Ethiopians, and Aïda cries out, saying that she will weep for him forever. The passion with which she utters her cry completely convinces Amneris. She abandons her compassionate tone and accuses Aïda directly of being in love with Radamès—and to clinch the point, she now tells her that she has just lied: Radamès lives. The rapturous "Thank God" that greets this news makes Amneris put their rivalry into so many words: she, the Pharaoh's daughter, is Aïda's rival. Does Aïda understand this?

Hopelessly Aïda kneels before her mistress, begging for pity, but she gets only threats of vengeance and hatred. Their voices rise together in a powerful duet which is suddenly interrupted by trumpets and a chorus off stage singing the war chorus of Act I. The duet comes to a climax as Amneris commands her slave to follow her to the ceremonies and see whether she has any chance of being a successful rival. The Princess sweeps angrily and regally off the stage, while Aïda remains behind long enough to utter once more the pitiful close of her Act I prayer.

Act Two, Scene 2

THE second scene of the second act of *Aïda* is the grandest grand opera one is likely to see. With the Theban temple of Ammon on one side of the stage and a throne with a purple canopy on the other, the producers pour out everything the treasury affords—armies, captives, priests, dancers, religious symbols, elephants, horses, and the Theban Brass Band. All of these come in, one after the other, the King leading Amneris to the throne, palm-bearers waving them on, and a ballet dancing a dance of victory. The chorus sings, the horses prance, and the brass band plays the familiar Triumphal March peering through anachronistic spectacles at the modern notes attached to modern instruments (see p. 283). (For some reason, the band players, unlike the chorus, are not expected to know their music by heart.) Yet, however absurd many of the details may appear, however many tales are told of the ludicrous mishaps to the insufficiently rehearsed animals and supernumeraries, the scene is almost invariably effective. And however striking the music Verdi wrote for this colorful pageantry, he had still more striking ensemble music to write for the dramatic developments of the scene.

The final part of the triumphal procession is headed by Radamès drawn in a chariot. The King descends to greet the savior of the people, and Amneris (while the orchestra plays her characteristic theme, No. 3) places a crown upon his head. Anything Radamès asks, says the King, will be granted, and the first request is to have the prisoners brought forth. They come sadly trooping in while the priests softly chant their thanks to God. Last among the captives, wearing a lionskin and two large horns on his head to show his rank of officer, comes Amonasro. Aïda, who has been carefully scanning the procession, rushes to him with the cry "My father!" but in a quick aside he tells her not to betray his name or his real rank.

The King calls on Amonasro to step forward, and he identifies himself simply as a man who has fought and in defeat sought vainly for death. Then, with a fierce, regal dignity, he begins what is one of the most overpowering ensembles in all grand opera. He reports that the King of Ethiopia has been killed in the battle and swears angrily that if fighting for one's fatherland is a crime, they are all ready for death. Yet, he adds softly, in a warm melody, let the King now show mercy, for who knows what may happen tomorrow? His plea is taken up by the prisoners and by Aïda, but Ramphis and the priests step forward demanding death for all of them. Their stern, almost stertorous, melody is punctuated with cries for mercy from the Ethiopians, and the King and other Egyptians soon join in, also on the side of mercy. Meantime, Radamès again sees Aïda, and Amneris once more notes that her rival is being preferred; for Radamès cannot bear to see Aïda in tears: they seem rather to make him love her more than ever. All these conflicting passions are expressed simultaneously; and though the individual words cannot be understood, the dramatic situation is completely clear and the mounting music (there are eighteen simultaneous vocal lines in the score) makes an unforgettable pattern of sound (see p. 288).

This ensemble over, Radamès makes his request of the King: let all the Ethiopian prisoners be freed. Ramphis, however, steps forward to argue the inexpediency of such a step. Once freed, he fears the Ethiopians will fight again. Again the priests join their leader in his pleas; again the general population is on the side of leniency. Finally, Ramphis proposes a compromise: let the common prisoners be freed, but let Aïda's father be held. The King, delighted with a compromise, agrees to this and then turns to the victorious Radamès and tells him that he shall marry Amneris and rule after him. Radamès is too thunderstruck to say a word, though Amneris has time for an aside expressive of her triumph over Aïda. The slaves and the people join in a chorus praising Egypt respectively for its clemency and its victory; the priests, led by Ramphis, praise Isis; Radamès and Aïda, recovered from the shock of the King's announcement, express their consternation; and Amneris turns from her private triumph over Aïda to expressing her joy in being promised to Radamès. The King says nothing much more than *"Gloria!"* Amonasro, in the general rejoicing going on around him, tells Aïda that all hope for the fatherland is not yet lost, and the act closes with a surge of music that is scarcely less exciting than the great climax reached a short while before.

Act Three

THE third act, known as the "Nile Scene," takes place the night before Amneris and Radamès are to be married. Palm trees line the bank of the river, which can be seen glistening in the moonlight on the back of the stage, while to one side, on a hill of granite rocks, stands the temple of Isis in Memphis. The brief introductory music—very quiet and simple—suggests the lapping of the water. Within the temple a chorus, led by a high priestess, again chants a prayer (see p. 281).

A boat glides up to the banks of the river, for Ramphis is leading Amneris to the temple to pray to Isis the night before her marriage. They are attended by veiled women and guards, and Amneris enters the temple, saying that she will pray that Radamès may learn to love her as she does him.

With the stage empty again, the lapping of the water is still suggested by a monotonous, murmuring figure in the middle strings, and over it Aïda's theme (No. 1) is quietly played by the first violins. Heavily veiled, she comes in to keep a secret rendezvous with Radamès. If he plans only to tell her good-bye, says Aïda, she will drown herself in the Nile. In her second great aria, the *"O Patria mia,"* she then gives voice to her other fierce longing—that for her native land (see p. 291).

But instead of Radamès, it is her father who meets her. He has been watching, he says, and nothing escapes his attention. He knows that Aïda and Radamès are deeply in love, that she is waiting for him now, and that her rival is the daughter of the Pharaohs, Amneris. "And I, the daughter of Amonasro, am in her power," says Aïda; but Amonasro assures her that it need not be so, that she can still return to her country and have both her throne and her Radamès. In a warm duet, they sing of the day in which such joy can be achieved; and Amonasro recalls to her how the Egyptians had attacked Ethiopia, desecrated their altars, raped the virgins, and murdered mothers, old men, and children. Aïda prays that they may return once more to a happy homeland—and Amonasro now thinks he has her in the right frame of mind to fall in with his plot.

The Ethiopians, he tells her, are ready to strike again. All they need to know is the path by which the enemy is preparing to march—and it is up to Aïda to discover it. Radamès, the leader of the Egyptians, is to meet her here, and Radamès loves Aïda.

It takes just a moment for Aïda to grasp that Amonasro is suggesting that she betray Radamès. She recoils from her father, crying, "No! no! never!"

Her refusal drives Amonasro to savage fury. With great violence he repulses Aïda and describes the attack of the Egyptian cohorts, the destruction and death that will come to the Ethiopian towns. "Do you see?" he cries. "From the deep come ghosts accusing you of murdering your fatherland; and there is one horrible one pointing a bony arm at your head; your mother's arm, cursing you!"

Pitilessly he ignores his daughter's pleas for mercy and throws her to the ground. She is not his daughter, he cries, but a slave of the Pharaohs.

It is more than she can stand. She drags herself to his feet. The music subsides to soft but agitatedly syncopated repetitions of the same note to suggest her excited grief, and she consents to do what he asks. Then, in a broad, noble melody he takes her to his heart, bidding her think of the great service she is doing her people, and very, very softly (Verdi's marking is *ppppp*) she sighs how dear her love of country costs her. Amonasro, hearing Radamès approach, gives her a word of encouragement and hides himself among the palms (see p. 295).

Radamès' first phrase (marked *con transporto*) is a burst of rapture on seeing Aïda once more:

No. 9
Allegro

Once more I see＿＿ you, my dear A - i - da!
Pur ti ri - veg - go, mia dol-ce A - i - da!

But Aïda is now inclined to be analytical. She points out that he is to marry Amneris; and no matter how much he swears that he loves only Aïda, how can he go against the King, the people, and the priests? Radamès tells her that war is once more in the offing; the Ethiopians have again arisen and already crossed the Egyptian borders. He, Radamès, is to be the general against them, and when he wins his victory, he will tell the King that all he wants is to marry Aïda. Radamès, however, is reckoning without Amneris, as the more astute Aïda points out, while the orchestra plays the theme associated with Amneris' jealousy (No. 4). Her revenge would fall on both Aïda and Amonasro, and there would be nothing Radamès could do about it. Still, if Radamès really loves Aïda, as he says he does, there is a way——. And she sings him a ravishing description of the new country whither they could fly away together. Radamès finds the prospect enchanting enough, but his soldierly soul cannot accept the idea of deserting his own country—the country he has fought for, the country that has given him his first taste of glory, the sky that has looked over their love. How can he forget that? Aïda repeats her description, and their voices blend in the ensuing duet (see p. 298).

Finally, when Aïda sees that she is not getting anywhere, she tells him to go; he does not love her, despite his protests. Let him marry his Amneris, and let the ax fall on her and her father. This last argument makes Radamès suddenly change his determination. Taking his courage in his hands, he agrees to go, his decision giving rise to one more fine duet (which usually is sung much too loud). They agree to run away to Aïda's own land, and just as they are about to go off she asks what way they will take to avoid the military.

"The path," says Radamès, " by which we shall fall on the enemy tomorrow. It will be deserted till then."

"And what path is that?"

"The gorges of Napata."

At this point Amonasro jumps out of his hiding place and triumphantly announces that he will place his men at the gorges of Napata—and he reveals himself to Radamès not only as Aïda's father but as Amonasro, the King of Ethiopia. At first Radamès cannot believe him, but in the trio that follows, Amonasro assures him that no blame can be attached to him—it was the will of fate. Meanwhile Aïda tries to console him, while he cries despairingly over his lost honor.

Amonasro is trying to drag off the reluctant Radamès when Amneris comes from the temple, followed by Ramphis and the guards. The Ethiopian king attacks Amneris with his dagger, but Radamès stops him and urges him to fly with his daughter. Then, as Ramphis orders the soldiers to capture the fleeing pair, Radamès turns to him and, with a despairing but heroic gesture, offers his sword in surrender.

Act Four, Scene 1

IT IS now the day on which Radamès is to be tried for treason. In a passage near his cell, Amneris is waiting. Through this passage Radamès and the priests who are to try him will pass, and from it Amneris can see into the hall of justice.* Aïda, she tells us in recitative, has escaped, and Radamès is to be tried as a traitor, though he is no more a traitor than Aïda is. Both deserve death, she cries. But what is she saying? The orchestra plays the dignified but very feminine theme associated with her calmer moods (No. 3), and she says that she will always love him no matter how so insane a love destroys her life. And now she will try to save him—and she commands the guards to bring Radamès to her.

When the guards have led in the prisoner, Amneris tells him that she can still save him by pleading with her father. Her mood and the music accompanying it are solemn and earnest; and in the same mood, to the same music, Radamès replies that he has no interest at all in defending himself (see p. 302). In the eyes of the gods he is guiltless, and he has no further interest in living. Then, in a more animated, flowing melody, Amneris pleads with him to live for her sake, for Amneris, who has suffered so much that she is ready to give up her country and throne for him. Again taking up her melody, Radamès (obviously in no mood for either tact or com-

promise) points out that he too has given up his country—and his honor as well—for Aïda. Amneris herself, he says, is responsible for his misery, for she has killed Aïda.

Neither Amneris nor the audience knows just where he got this piece of misinformation, and Amneris immediately proceeds to correct it. It is true that Amonasro was killed in the defeat of the Ethiopians, she tells him, but Aïda just disappeared, and no one has heard of her since. "May the gods guide her safe to her country," breathes Radamès, "and keep her from knowing that I am dying for her."†

Amneris, however, wants to stick to the point. She offers Radamès life if only he will swear never to see Aïda as long as he lives. Radamès cannot be moved. As the duet reaches its

---

*According to the score, the hall of justice should be to the left of the stage; but in many modern productions it is below it, with an opening in the center of the stage through which Amneris can watch the proceedings. This arrangement is both more workable and more dramatic than the original one.

†In the eleven bars of this brief prayer, Verdi comes as near as anywhere in the opera to using the Wagnerian device of transforming a theme in order to suggest an idea expressed earlier in the opera. Quotation (a) below is from the first-act "Celeste Aïda"; quotation (b) is the present passage:

climax, he insists that he now gladly goes to his death knowing that he has given his life for Aïda's; while Amneris, baffled by such strength of will, frantically cries that heaven will see that she gets revenge for her suffering. Completely overcome by his obstinacy, she sinks to the ground, and Radamès is led off by the guards.

The solemn, relentless theme of the priests (No. 2) is now heard in the low strings. Amneris, covering her face with her hands and choking with remorse, moans that she herself, by her jealousy, has sealed his doom. The priests file across the stage on their way to the judgment hall, but Amneris cannot bear to look upon what she calls "these white phantoms." From below they chant an unaccompanied prayer that the gods may kindle their hearts with the light of justice; and as Amneris continues her wretched moaning, Radamès is led from the opposite side, also into the hall of justice. He does not even glance at her.

The brief trial begins. We hear Ramphis accusing Radamès first of deserting camp the day before battle, and second of betraying his country, his king, and his honor. After each accusation, the priests call on him to exonerate himself. Both times there is complete silence except for a low rumbling in the drums; both times Amneris, in a despairing, descending phrase, calls on the gods to save him:

No. 10
Allegro

Ah,— pi-ty,   he— is not guilty, Ah, pi - ty,— ye— Gods spare,spare him.
Ah pie-tà!—   egli è inno-cen-te, Nu - mi, pie - tà,— Nu - mi, pie - tà.

Then the priests, led by Ramphis, pronounce sentence: Radamès, guilty of treason, is to be buried alive beneath the altar of the god he has failed to honor.

Again the priests cross the stage, their hands folded across their chests, still calling out solemnly: "Traitor! traitor! traitor!" Amneris rises to confront them, to tell them that she loves Radamès, and to curse them roundly for condemning an innocent man, for violating all the laws of earth and heaven, for being "infamous tigers." Through all this cursing, the priests merely repeat, over and over, "He is a traitor. He shall die." And even after they have filed off the stage again, we hear them repeating the same words, while Amneris works herself up to a wild rage with her vain curses upon them.

Act Four, Scene 2

THE last scene shows two levels. Below is the small, dark crypt into which Radamès has just been led to suffer his uncomfortable death, while above we see the interior of the temple of Vulcan, with large statues of Osiris brightly lighted, and two priests setting the stone in place that covers the crypt below.

"And that is my tomb," says Radamès; and he breathes a soft wish that Aïda may be happy wherever she is and never hear of his horrible end. Then he hears a sigh and sees what he first takes to be a vision. But it is no vision: somehow Aïda has managed to creep into the tomb ahead of Radamès, as she now comes forward and quietly tells him. Passionately, but with great tenderness, Radamès cries out against the horror that one so beautiful, so made for love, should die on account of him. Aïda, however, experiences none of this horror. Already almost transfigured, she seems to see the bright angel of death hovering over them and the gates of heaven opening. Above, the priests and priestesses chant their praises of Phthà —the same chant that had been used in the same temple to bless Radamès before he went to battle (No. 6). Using all his remaining power, Radamès tries to move the stone above him, but he cannot—and the chant goes on.

Then Aïda sings her last, beautiful farewell to earth (see p. 307). Radamès joins her; and as their voices rise in this supremely moving ending, Amneris comes in, throws herself on the stone above the crypt, and murmurs a final prayer for her beloved Radamès. Below, her rival quietly dies in his arms as the priests go on with their chanting.

Heavenly Aida

CELESTE AIDA

Queen of — my heart, Oh reign there for-re-
del mio pen - sie - ro tu sei re -

ev - er, Fil - ling with beau - ty my dark - est
gi - na, tu di mia vi - ta sei lo splen -

hour;
dor.

Could we re - turn to the land — that
Il tuo bel cie - lo vor - rei ri -

bore you, Where gen - tle breez - es come drift - ing
dar - ti, le dol - ci brez - ze del pa - trio

with mounting excitement

down; I would en - throne you, lay all be -
suol: un re - gal ser - to sul crin po -

build to the climax

fore you, Give you the sun - light to be your
sar - ti, er - ger - ti un tro - no vi - ci - no al

crown, Ah! Heav'n - ly A -
sol, ah! Ce - le - ste A -

(as though talking to himself)

Guard the Nile

SU! DEL NILO

friend us, Pray O - si - ris that he de - fend us, Pray the gods that they may
men - ti ch'es - si _ reg - go - no glie - ven - ti, che in po - ter de' Nu - mi

CHORUS

lend us Strength for ev - 'ry E - gyp - tian sword. Guard the
so - lo stan le sor - ti _ del guer - rier. Su! del

Nile's re - mot - est _ reach - es from the bold in - vad - ing _ horde; Drive the
Ni - lo al sa - cro li - do ac - cor - re - te, E - gi - zii e - roi. Da o - gni

staccato

foe - men from _ her _ beach - es, give them de - struc - tion and death for their re - ward!
cor pro - rom - pa un _ gri - do: guer - ra, _ guer - ra e mor - te al - lo stra - nier!

) 276 (

There Is No Other

E L'AMOR MIO? (RITORNA VINCITOR)

Original key: F

Andante

AIDA

There is no oth - er,
E l'a - mor mi - o?

p singing tone

Ped. Ped. Ped.

Ah,_____ how am I to smoth - er   The flame   of de-
Dun - que scor-dar pos-s'i - o   que-sto fer - vi - do a-

Ped. Ped. Ped. Ped. Ped.

vo - tion   that comes to   cheer   me, That warms   me   like   the
mo - re   che op-pres - sa e   schiava,___   co - me   rag - gio   di

) 277 (

sun,___ when__ he is near me. And shall I pray for death to him I
sol___ qui__ mi be - a - va? Im-pre-che - rò la mor-te a Ra-da-

love with love that is un - dy-ing? Ah!___ was there ev-er a
mès a lui ch'a-mo pur tan-to! Ah!___ non fu in ter - ra

heart so torn be - tween two___ loves be-yond de - ny-ing!
mai da più cru-de - - li an - go-scie un co-re af-fran-to!

legato

A soft expressive prayer

Gods of my youth, hear me a - gain,
Nu - mi, pie - tà del mio sof - frir!

Most Mighty Phtha
POSSENTE FTHÀ

Ah!_____ Hear as we call_____
ah!_____ noi t'in-vo-chia _ _

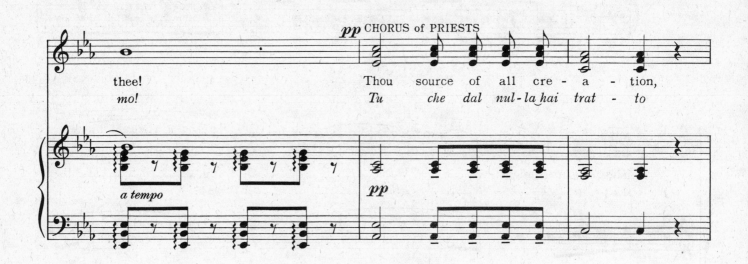

thee! Thou source of all cre - a - tion,
mo! Tu che dal nul-la_hai trat - to

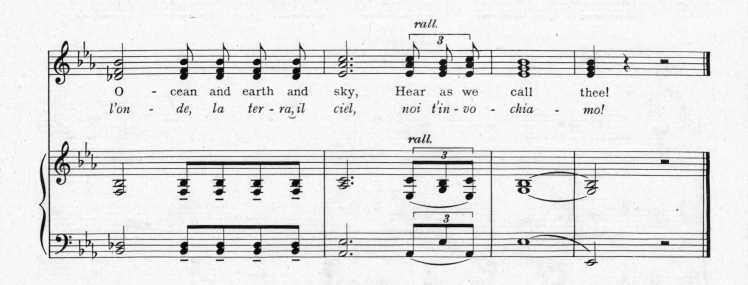

O - cean and earth and sky, Hear as we call thee!
l'on - de, la ter-ra,_il ciel, noi t'in-vo-chia - mo!

Glory to Egypt and Grand March
GLORIA ALL' EGITTO

Allegro *(majestically)*

Original keys: E-flat and A-flat

Glo - ry to E - gypt's might - y gods, Glo - ry for our sal -
Glo - ria all' E - git - to, ad I - si - de che il sa - cro suol pro -

va - tion! Sing hymns of ju - bi - la - tion To him who rules our
teg - ge! Al Re che il Del - ta reg - ge, al Re che il Del - ta

na - - tion, To our vic - to - rious king! En -
reg - - ge in - ni fe - sto - si al - ziam! S'in-

twine   a crown   of   lau - - rel and lo - tus____ for   the
trec - *ci il lo* - *to al* *lau* - - *ro sul crin dei____ vin* - *ci*-

he - ro,   O bring   your gar - lands near,_____ O____
to - *ri!*   *nem* - *bo* *gen* - *til*   *di fio* - *ri*____

cov - er the sword and____ spear!   Then dance,_____ E - gyp-tian
sten - *da sull' ar* - *mi un____ vel!*   *Dan* - *ziam,_____ fan-ciul-le e*-

maid - ens,   And raise_____ your voic - es bright - ly,
gi - *zie,*   *le mi* - *sti-che ca* - *ro* - *le,*

) 284 (

Like morn-ing stars that light - ly Dance when the sun- beams ap-pear.
co - me d'in-tor-no al so - le dan - za - no gli a - stri in ciel.

(Trumpets on stage)

Ah, Great King

MA TU, RE

Original key

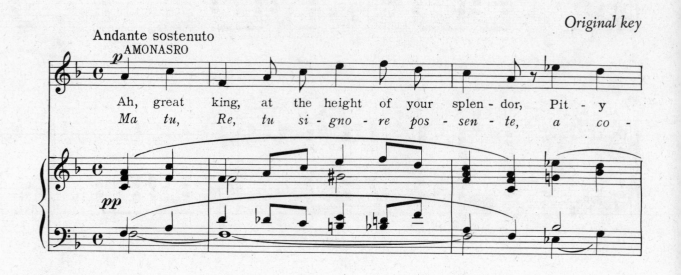

Andante sostenuto

AMONASRO

Ah, great king, at the height of your splen - dor, Pit - y
Ma tu, Re, tu si - gno - re pos - sen - te, a co -

us who are forced to sur - rend - er; Though to - day an - gry fate has be -
sto - ro ti vol - gi cle - men - te, Og - gi noi siam per - cos - si dal

trayed us, Ah, who___ can___ prom - ise what to - mor - row may
fa - to, ah, do - man___ voi po - tria il fa - to col -

Land of My Youth
O PATRIA MIA

Original key: F

softly, warmly

O land of a- zure skies with fra- grant warm _____
O cie- li az- zur- ri, o dol- ci au- re na- ti -

breeze, Land of my child- hood, bright hap- py days of
ve, do- ve se- re- no il mio mat- tin bril -

yore. O smil- ing val- leys, O laugh- ing lit- tle
lò. O ver- di col- li, o pro- fu- ma- te

riv- ers, Land of my child- hood, fare- well for ev- er-
ri- ve, O pa- tria mi- a, mai più ti ri- ve-

more!
drò!

with expression

O hap - py___
O pa - tria___

home - land, fare - well, ah___ fare -
mi - a, mai più, ah___ mai

well, fare - well,___ fare - well___ for ev - er -
più, ma - - i più___ ti ri - ve -

cresc.

more! Land of my youth, O hap - py
drò! O pa - tria mia, o pa - tria

p

cresc.

I Was Never a Slave

PADRE! A COSTORO

Original key: B-flat minor

I am your daugh - ter,
an - cor tua fi - glia

as you have known ____ me,
po - trai chia - mar - mi,

I love my coun - try, and I am
del - la mia pa - tria, del - la mia

wor - thy ___ to serve by your side.
pa - tria ___ de - gna sa - rò.

AMONASRO

Ah, ___ then re - mem - ber
Pen - sa che un po - po -

how her cause has fall — en. You, you a — lone can up-lift her
lo vin — to, stra — zia — to, per te sol — tan — to, per te sol —

AIDA

heart and re-store her pride. Be-lov — ed home — land, how great the
tan — to ri — sor — ger può. O patria! o pa — tria! quan — to mi

sac — — ri-fice, how dear the price that you have cost
co — — sti! O pa — tri — a! quan-to mi co —

AMONASRO

me! He's com-ing, have cour-age! Now, let me hide!
sti! Co-rag-gio! ei giun-ge,— là tut-to u-drò.

Where the Age-old Forest Sleeps

LÀ TRA FORESTE VERGINI

Original key: B-flat

I Could Defend Myself

DI MIE DISCOLPE

Original key: E-flat minor

though___ I re-vealed the se - cret, In words_____ un-wise - ly
fer - - se il lab-bro in-cau - to fa - tal_____ se-gre-to, é

spok - en, My faith_____ is still_ un-bro - ken, My faith is still un -
ve - ro, ma pu - ro il mio_ pen - sie - ro, ma pu-ro il mio pen-

bro - ken, My hon - or still re - mains. You'll die, then?
sie - ro e l'o - nor mio re - stò. Mo - ri - re!

AMNERIS

A little faster

Ah,_____ you must live for me,___
Ah!_____ tu dei vi - - ve - re!___

love   fills   my eyes   with   weep - ing,   My
glia - i   le not - ti in   pian - to—   *e*

grandly

king - - - dom,   my   coun - - - try,   my
pa - - - tria,   e   tro - - - no, e———

throne———   or   my   life,———————
tro - - no,   e   vi - - ta,

Ah,———   could   you   love———   me,   I   would
tut - - - to,   da - re - i,   tut - to,

give _____ all the world a - way!
tut - - to da - rei per te,

RADAMÈS

A - i - - da is my
Per es - - sa an - ch'io la

king - - dom, my hon - - or and my
pa - - tria, per es - - sa an - ch'io la

life, _____ Yes, _____ for my
pa - - tria e _____ l'o - nor

love, _____ I have al - read - y cast the world a - way!
mio, _____ e l'o - nor mi - o tra - di - a. _____

Oh Earth, Farewell

O TERRA ADDIO

light to guide us on our___ way;___ Now dawns at last a bright un-end-ing
ciel e l'al-me er-ran - ti___ vo - la-no al rag - gio del - l'e-ter - no

day.   AIDA A light, a light, RADAMÈS A light, a light, BOTH A heav'n-ly
dì.   il ciel, il ciel,   il ciel, il ciel,   si schiu-de il

light,___   A bright - er day. AMNERIS Peace, I im-plore you,
ciel,___   si schiu-de il ciel. Pa - ce t'im-plo - ro,

cross hands

AMNERIS
Oh, God, for - give me,   Heaven grant me   peace!___
pa - ce t'im-plo - ro,   pa - ce, pa - ce,   pa - ce!

cross hands

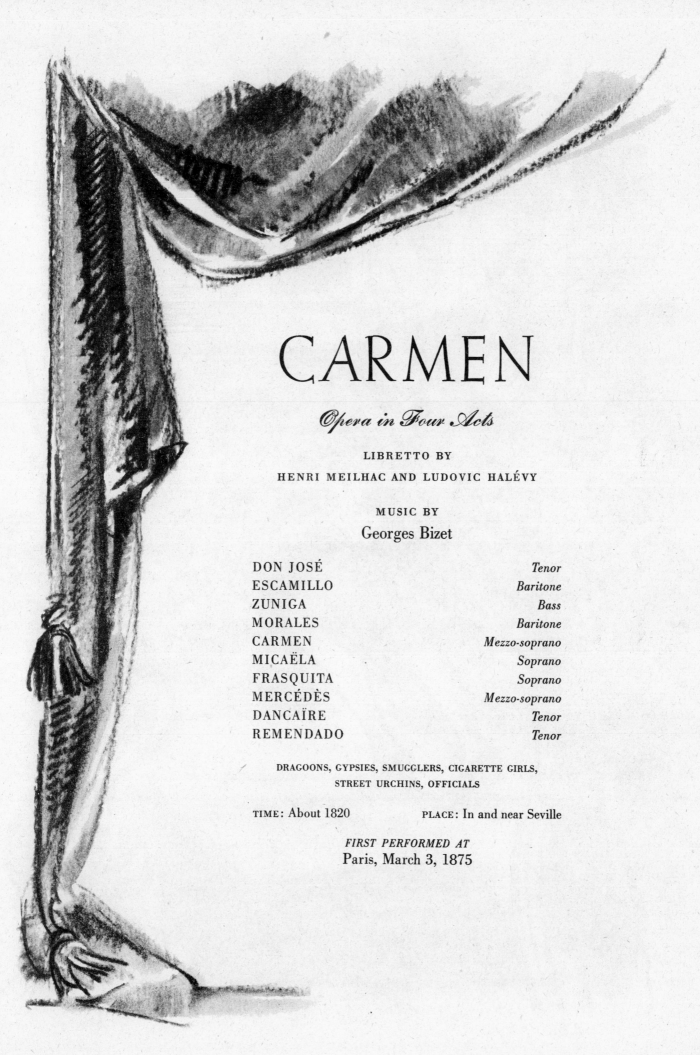

CARMEN

Opera in Four Acts

LIBRETTO BY
HENRI MEILHAC AND LUDOVIC HALÉVY

MUSIC BY
Georges Bizet

DON JOSÉ	*Tenor*
ESCAMILLO	*Baritone*
ZUNIGA	*Bass*
MORALES	*Baritone*
CARMEN	*Mezzo-soprano*
MICAËLA	*Soprano*
FRASQUITA	*Soprano*
MERCÉDÈS	*Mezzo-soprano*
DANCAÏRE	*Tenor*
REMENDADO	*Tenor*

DRAGOONS, GYPSIES, SMUGGLERS, CIGARETTE GIRLS,
STREET URCHINS, OFFICIALS

TIME: About 1820   PLACE: In and near Seville

FIRST PERFORMED AT
Paris, March 3, 1875

Carmen

GEORGES BIZET

I T IS not true, as one of the stuffier legends of opera reports, that Bizet died of a broken heart because *Carmen* failed in its first season at the Paris Opéra-Comique. He did die three months after its *première* on March 3, 1875, but he was already ill before that *première;* and the opera itself, while no outstanding success in the beginning, had fifty performances at the Opéra-Comique before it was a year old. Then it was shelved at that house and not revived for seven years, during which time it became so popular in other French cities, as well as in England, Germany, and Italy, that the company was practically forced to revive it. Since then it has been a staple of the repertoire at the Opéra-Comique and in practically every other opera house in the world. After *Faust* it is the most popular French opera in modern history, and today—in the United States, at least—it is rapidly overtaking the prodigious number of performances Gounod's masterpiece has had.

The reason some of its original critics did not take to the work at once was its violence and the unsavory, low-class character of its heroine. Literary critics apparently had stronger stomachs than opera critics in nineteenth-century France, for the original story of *Carmen,* by Prosper Mérimée (who died five years before the *première* of Bizet's opera), was generally regarded as an excellent piece of writing. And Mérimée's Carmen is a much more unsavory and low-class character than the heroine put into the libretto by Henri Meilhac and Ludovic Halévy.*

Meilhac and Halévy knew their business. Their Carmen, unlike Mérimée's, is not married to an unpleasant thug while carrying on with a soldier; she does not go in for picking watches out of strangers' pockets; she does not go in for fighting with knives and conniving at murder; nor does she give up Don José for a mere picador. Mérimée's heroine, they knew, had to be washed—if not scrubbed—before she could be made presentable to the Opéra-Comique. They did their

job with consummate skill: *Carmen* has just about as good a libretto as there is. Even so, the management disliked it right from the beginning. One member, named Leuven, summarized its point of view like this:

"Isn't she assassinated by her lover?" he asked Halévy. "At the Opéra-Comique! A family theater! A theater for the promotion of marriages! We rent five or six boxes every night for these meetings of young couples. You are going to put our audience to flight. No, it's impossible." He begged Halévy not to let Carmen die. "Death has never been seen on this stage, do you hear, never! Don't let her die, I beg of you, my dear child."

One reason for Leuven's horror, obviously, was that seventy years ago the word *comique* in Opéra-Comique really meant comedy and only operas with happy endings were performed. Since that time, some historians of music claim, the distinction between grand opera and *opéra comique* as given in Paris has come to mean that there are no spoken words in the former, while the latter has an appreciable amount of spoken dialogue. The distinction is almost valueless. For more than a generation the Opéra-Comique in Paris has included such works as *Tosca* and *Tristan et Isolde* in its repertoire, neither of which has spoken dialogue and both of which have very, very sad endings. Yet, with *Carmen* the French maintain this distinction by giving it in its original form—that is, with a good deal of spoken dialogue.†

If Paris was slow in appreciating one of the finest operas ever composed, the United States had its doubts too. When an Italian version reached New York's Academy of Music in 1878, the critic for the *Tribune* called the plot "almost offensive in its combined puerility and brutality," while Cincinnati and Cleveland critics dis-

---

*This Halévy should not be confused with his uncle, Jacques Halévy, Bizet's father-in-law and the composer of *La Juive.*

†The spoken portions were set to recitative for the first performance in Vienna, a little over seven months after the Paris *première,* by Ernest Guiraud, a French composer who happened to be born in New Orleans. He also put the finishing touches on Offenbach's *Tales of Hoffmann.* At the Metropolitan Opera in New York a small amount of spoken dialogue is now used in *Carmen.* This, unfortunately, takes place between Carmen and her smuggling associates while Don José sings his soldier's song, *"Man of Alcalá,"* off stage. At the Metropolitan, therefore, the only time you can really hear this fine tune is in the Prelude to the second act.

liked it for moral reasons. Today both critics and public have hardier moral stomachs, stomachs that calmly digest even such unpleasant concoctions as *Salomé*. The Opéra-Comique has given *Carmen* well over twenty-two hundred times, and in 1940 the Metropolitan Opera Guild chose this tale of illicit love and brutal violence for its special children's matinees. America has also seen a Russian version called *Carmencita and the Soldier*, a Negro version called *Carmen Jones*, three motion-picture versions, and a bilingual performance in which Gertrud Wettergren, assuming the role at the Metropolitan on one day's notice, sang in Swedish while the rest of the cast sang in French.

Various reasons have been given for the enduring popularity of the opera. One is that it is so very Spanish. Spaniards usually deny this, and the opera has not been particularly popular in Spain. To non-Spanish ears, portions of the music certainly do sound like authentic local color, especially the Prelude to the last act. Yet there are many famous pages—like the "Flower Song" and the first-act duet between Don José and Micaëla—that sound no more Spanish than anything in *Faust*.

Another reason given for its popularity is the attraction of the title role for almost any female singer. It may be sung by either soprano or contralto, and some women have essayed it with practically no voice at all. It lends itself to more varieties of stage business than any other role in opera. Every new Carmen is in some ways different from the others, and a great deal of nonsense is issued by press agents about the latest one going back to study the original sources. The ultimate original source is, of course, Mérimée's story, and any singer who tried to be faithful to that would necessarily be unfaithful to the librettists of the opera. The success or lack of it seems to be directly proportional to the success the singer has in projecting across the footlights—both dramatically and musically—a convincing and attractive gypsy. So many early Carmens seem to have been so successful with this role that any contemporary singer has to conquer the conservative and sentimental memories of older operagoers, who will softly murmur about Minnie Hauk, Emma Calvé, Zélie de Lussan, Maria Gay, Olive Fremstad, or any one of half a dozen others. I happen to have heard none of these; but after thirty years of operagoing and over a score of Carmens, I am convinced that there neither can nor should be such a thing as a "definitive" interpretation of the role. The most vocally satisfying I remember was a Swedish soprano whom I heard in Stockholm but whose name I cannot recall; the most dramatically satisfying was, I think, Marguerite Sylva. But as it is seven years since I was in Stockholm and twenty since I heard Sylva, I won't trust my own memory any more than my even more ancient friends'. Carmen is so rich a role that it is almost as difficult to find a completely unsatisfying performance of it as it is to find a completely dull Hamlet.

Still another element contributing to the popularity of the opera is a few of its tunes. The *"Habañera"* and the Toreador Song* are now almost a part of our folk music. Yet one or two popular tunes are not enough to insure comparative immortality for any opera. Who recalls even the plot of Bishop's *Clari, the Maid of Milan,* in which "Home, Sweet Home" is the principal musical fare?

The ultimate cause for *Carmen*'s success lies, I think, in the public's excellent taste. *Carmen* is just about as nearly perfect an opera as there is. It has a good, vigorous, believable story; it has at least two three-dimensional characters; even its minor characters are sketched with complete credibility. It is good theater throughout, and the music not only refuses to get in its way, but it helps at every turn. It underlines the dramatic situations; it has tunes that are at once singable, memorable, and in character; it suggests vividly the bright color of the setting; its orchestration is brilliant without ever overshadowing the voices or the action. No other opera in the standard repertoire makes it at once so unmistakably clear what all the shooting and the shouting are about, and in few other operas do the shooting and the shouting seem to matter so much.

*The Toreador Song was actually inserted into the opera by Bizet over his own poorer judgment. He had written a more dignified aria for the baritone, which is said to have been out of character. When he turned up with the most popular baritone number in all opera, he remarked, "Ah well, they want filth. Here it is."

Prelude

IN THE bright key of A major, the Prelude to *Carmen* immediately sets the sunny, Spanish background for the tale of love and violence that is to follow. With cymbals crashing, the entire orchestra gives out the happy, vigorous, noisy, bustling tune which at the end of the opera is played with dramatic irony off stage:

No. 1
Allegro giocoso

It is followed by a softer theme still in the same character, used to accompany the change of guard in Act I.

No. 2
Allegro giocoso

There is a quick crescendo, and then No. 1 comes back.

Suddenly there is a startling change of key. The martial tune of the Toreador Song comes in softly played by the strings and then repeated *fortissimo* by the whole orchestra. Again No. 1 comes back, and Bizet seems to have set the background for his play with a picture of Spanish bullfighting in a nicely balanced little prelude.

But he has not quite finished. There is a dramatic pause, and the fiddles start a vigorous tremolo in minor. Then the cellos sing out the fateful theme that again and again is to suggest the irresistible but sinister attraction Carmen has for Don José.

No. 3
Andante moderato

It is worked up to a quick climax, and a short, loud diminished seventh chord leaves us hanging in suspense. Another dramatic pause—and the curtain rises.

Act One

ON THE right of a bright square in Seville is a cigarette factory, on the left a guardhouse, in back a bridge. There are people bustling about and soldiers lounging before the guardhouse. Their uniforms are of bright yellow and red, with shiny buttons, which the Spanish army wore in the early nineteenth century and which made them such excellent targets. Having nothing better to do, the soldiers comment on the attractive little scene before them—they smoke and joke, as their leader, Corporal Morales, puts it.

Then, to a little figure in triplets, Micaëla, a blonde, innocent-looking country maid, attracts the Corporal's eye. He asks her what she is looking for, and she says, "A corporal." The Corporal suggests with ogling gallantry, "That's me," but Micaëla knows it really isn't. Her particular corporal calls himself "Don José," she says. Do they know him? They all do. Unfortunately, he is not a member of this company, but he will come shortly with the changing of the guard. Meantime, won't the pretty little girl come into the guardhouse and wait for him? But Micaëla has been brought up too well for that; and when the soldiers become pressing, she manages to escape. Morales and the others shrug their shoulders and go back to eying the crowd with detached amusement.

It is a charming little opening for the opera, and latecomers miss no important part of the story. What they do miss is a delightful little march tune to which Morales and the soldiers inform Micaëla about the impending change of guard.

No. 4
Allegretto

The change of guard now takes place. An off-stage bugle call is echoed in the orchestra; a bugler and two fifers come on stage, heading a crowd of street urchins in ragged military formation; and then come Captain Zuniga, Corporal Don José, and their troop of dragoons who are to relieve Corporal Morales' company. While they go through their formalities—consummated in most opera houses with an effect of unconscious satire on the martial amenities of the Spanish army—the boys go through their own formations singing about their youthful military drill and its proud masculinity, *ta ra-ta-ta-ta ra-ta-ta*. It would be a little more convincing (but less amusing) if most opera companies did not find it necessary to eke out the volume of the youngsters' voices with a few experienced female choristers uncomfortably costumed like twelve-year-old gamins. The tune the fifes play and the youngsters sing is No. 2 from the Prelude.

During the change of guard, Morales informs Don José, with appreciative detail, of the charming miss who has been looking for him. Then the Corporal marches off with his company right out of the story.* But in a few pages Bizet has given us a complete little character vignette.

Corporal Don José is second in command to Captain Zuniga in the freshly mounted guard, and in a few lines of dialogue we get another pair of character sketches. José points out the factory to Zuniga, apparently a newcomer to these parts, and says that the girls in it have an interesting reputation. However, he hastily adds, he doesn't pay much attention to such things. Zuniga, quite a soldier-about-town, says he has heard all about it. As for Don José, there's that blonde from the country, Micaëla, eh? To which Don José replies with youthful pomposity that it's quite true, quite true, and he loves her. As for the working girls, let Zuniga cast his own eyes on their attractions—whereupon the young prig sits down on a chair and does his level best to pay no attention to the increasingly animated scene around him.

For the factory bell now sounds, the knowing young men of the town gather about the entrance as though it were a stage door, and frankly announce their intention of making the most of their noonday opportunities with these smoking *impudentes.*

---

*If you look carefully, you can see this engaging minor character as one of the merrymakers in Lillas Pastia's inn in the next act. He sings along with the tenors of the chorus.

No. 5
Allegro moderato

All of them smoking (quite a shocking detail in 1875), the girls come from the factory. They sing a sinuous melody suggestive of the smoke and comparing, like a dozen popular songs since, the evanescent smoke of a cigarette and the evanescent vows of love made by their gallants. But it is Carmen (*La Carmencita* they call her) for whom the men are really waiting. Suddenly she is announced in the orchestra by a quick, twisty little version of the theme that signalizes her fatal attractions (compare No. 3):

No. 6
Allegro moderato

"Carmen!" cry the tenors with operatic unanimity. "Tell us what day you are going to love us."

"Good Lord," she says characteristically, "I don't know. Maybe never, maybe tomorrow—but certainly not today." Then, with the co-operation of both the men and her fellow wage-slaves, she sings the *"Habañera,"* a popular Spanish dance, possibly Cuban in origin, with a definitely lascivious character (see p. 321).

Throughout the *"Habañera,"* Carmen tries to get Don José's eye, but he sits sullenly on one side, whittling a stick of wood and ostentatiously refusing to pay her any attention. When the song—and the applause—are over, the young men renew their pleas to her, but she makes one last effort to get the young noncom's attention. Still no luck—and then, to the accompaniment of No. 3, she takes a flower from her bodice and tosses it to him. He is terribly embarrassed, and while everybody laughs at him and the factory bell sounds again, they leave him alone to pick up the flower. "What a witch!" he says.

Now Micaëla comes back, and José greets her at once—not with a kiss but with a request that she tell him about his mother. All the way through the opera, in fact, he is more drawn to his village mother than to his village sweetheart. The two engage in a most melodious duet, their voices twining in and out together—all in praise of José's home and mother (see p. 324). In the middle of it (but this part is usually cut), he recalls the threat to his peace of mind that Carmen had presented, and thanks heaven that the kiss his mother has sent him has averted that peril. Micaëla gives José a maternal letter as well as a maternal kiss and modestly retires to let him read it by himself. This he does to a melody from the recently completed duet, promising that he will marry Micaëla. "As for your flowers, you witch—" he is beginning, when there is a terrific racket in the factory.

All the girls stream out of the factory, and the guards, headed by Zuniga, stream out of the guardhouse. It seems that there has been a hair-pulling match inside. A girl named Manuela had said she was going to buy an ass, and Carmen had remarked that she didn't need to ride an ass when she was so expert on a broom. One word led to another and to violence, and now they are all trying to tell Zuniga their versions at once. The Captain really rather enjoys all this feminine attention, but he does his soldierly duty. He has his troops clear the square and orders José with two guards to go in and see what the trouble is.* Presently the Corporal comes back leading Carmen, who is in high spirits. She gaily refuses to answer Zuniga's questions, rubs up against him, and repeatedly sings a dancy phrase with, as Bizet put it in the score, *la plus grande impertinence*. The Captain is not unmindful of Carmen's attractions, but he thinks on the whole she'd better cool off in jail for a while. He orders Don José to take her there and retires to the guardhouse.

While Don José ties Carmen's hands behind her back and seats her on a chair, she tells him confidently that, on account of the flower she threw him earlier, he is going to help her escape. He, however, only tells her to shut up, and so she goes

to work on him in earnest. Still seated on the chair, her hands still tied, she sings the "*Seguidilla*" (see p. 324), inviting a certain young officer who is no captain, no lieutenant, but only a corporal, to come to her friend Lillas Pastia's inn and take the place of her recently dismissed lover. Don José tries to shush her, but she says she is only singing a song to herself and thinking—and thinking certainly cannot be forbidden. But she sees that her clearly expressed "thoughts" are working on this country fellow, and with one more stanza he is won over. Does she really mean it? Will she love him? Will she be faithful? Yes, says Carmen—and Don José loosens the cords. Then triumphantly swinging them, she sings her song once more, hurrying back to the chair and putting her arms behind her just before Zuniga returns from the guardhouse.

The Captain has made out the order for taking Carmen to jail and gives it to Don José with a warning to take care. She whispers instructions to her young man, sings a challenging phrase or two from the "*Habañera*" to Zuniga, and the plot is carried out as they reach the bridge. She turns around, gives José a shove, and, swinging the ties that bind her no longer, runs off as everyone laughs. As the curtain goes down, Don José ruefully picks himself up and surrenders to Zuniga.

Act Two

THE short Prelude to Act II is given over to the little soldier song Don José sings later on as he returns from prison (see p. 340), a short contrasting passage, and a repetition of the

In a recent performance at the Lewisohn Stadium in New York City, under the stage direction of Herbert Graf, no doubt was left in the minds of the audience as to who had won the fight. Manuela was carried across the stage by the two guards, completely unconscious. Even this couldn't make anything but a comparative sissy of Carmen, for in Mérimée's story she whips out her knife and slashes a deep X on Manuela's forehead.

soldier song with simple chromatic counterpoint in the cellos.

The act takes place at night at Lillas Pastia's inn on the outskirts of Seville—the gay spot Carmen had described for Don José in the Act I "*Seguidilla*." It also serves as a rendezvous for a gang of smugglers.

A lively drinking-and-dancing party is in progress, dominated by gypsies, who include Carmen and her two gypsy intimates, Frasquita and Mercédès. Captain Zuniga is a prominent member of the group, and it is obvious that in the two months that have passed since he ordered Carmen's arrest he has succumbed to her charms without making a great deal of progress in his suit. She is just having him on, as our British cousins put it.

The scene starts with a gypsy song led by Carmen, joined in by Frasquita and Mercédès and then by the whole chorus. The ballet dances a gypsy dance meanwhile, and at the speeded-up end of the number Carmen is supposed to join in with them. Many Carmens conscientiously wave their arms and take a few steps, but few of them fail to be shown up by even the most second-rate ballet troupe. Irra Petina, the Metropolitan's Russo-American mezzo, is one of the exceptions.

The dance over, Frasquita reports that Lillas Pastia says the sheriff has told him it's closing time. Zuniga, trying to get in the good graces of the girls, invites them to come along with him, but they refuse; they have other business. As one last effort to win a smile from Carmen, the Captain then tells her that her soldier-boy friend has now been released from prison. "Fine," says Carmen, "and now, good night."

But a chorus off stage interrupts them, hailing Escamillo, a popular matador who had won a famous victory over a bull at Granada. Even before Escamillo makes his brilliant entrance, Zuniga shouts an invitation to a drink, and then Escamillo comes on followed by a crowd of his fans and sings the Toreador Song (see p. 334). It describes the bullfight in detail, and the famous refrain refers to the dark eyes that await the hero. Any baritone with the proper swagger and skill with his cloak can make a great hit with it, even though he may (as many baritones do) ruin the melodic lines of the piece by huffing and puffing instead of singing it. He uses his cloak to describe the fight, and he uses Carmen to indicate the dark eyes that wait for him. While he does the first, the chorus effectively echoes and supports him; while he does the second, he really succumbs to the obvious attractions of Carmen. And so at the end of the song (in a passage many opera companies omit), he expressively sings the words "*l'amour*" to Mercédès, to Frasquita, and to Carmen, but with a special little turn for the last. Then, just before his triumphant exit, he makes a quick offer of his love to her. It is rejected with inviting finality: Carmen is thinking of a certain soldier.

Everyone follows Escamillo out except Carmen, Frasquita, Mercédès, and a couple of fine young gypsy smugglers named El Remendado and El Dancairo. One of the most skillful and colorful quintets in opera follows. It begins like this:

No. 7
Allegro vivo

and goes along at a tremendous clip, with the tune tossed from one voice to another so that no reasonably simple piano trans-

cription could approach its delightful effect, wherefore it is omitted in our selections. Remendado and Dancaïre (to give him his French name) have plans afoot which are never described further than the contention of the two gallants that deceiving and thieving of whatever kind need the co-operation of women. Therefore they'd like the three girls to join them. The girls acknowledge the soft impeachment and are delighted to join in, no questions asked—that is, all except Carmen. "Sorry," she says, "I'm not leaving here," and when pressed for a reason, she says she is in love—one of the most astonishing bits of unreason, the two men say, they have ever heard. To a light, ironic melody,

No. 8
Allegro

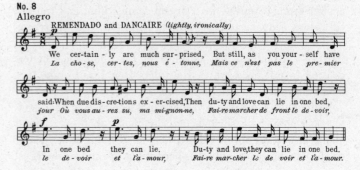

they tell her this isn't the first time she's been in love, and besides she's a past master at combining love and duty. Carmen replies in the same tune, but she is firm.

Just then Don José is heard approaching, singing his soldier song off stage (see p. 340). The gypsies peer out at him and tease Carmen about what a fine-looking fellow he is and what a good addition he would make to the party. Carmen manages to get them out of the room only by promising to try to persuade him to join the smuggling band. Thereupon Don José, once more in uniform, makes his entry on the high G that ends the repetition of his song.

"At last! Carmen!" are his first words as he comes in. He tells her he has been in prison for two months and would be glad to be there still if it were for her; and he shows his first signs of jealousy when he learns that some of the officers have been around making the girls dance for them. Carmen soothes him by promising to dance entirely in his honor and make her own music for it. She seats him comfortably on a chair and begins a slow, provocative dance to a sinuous melody without words, accompanying herself on the castanets (see p. 342). Faintly off stage the retreat bugles sound, and Don José does not notice them at once. When he does, his automatic reaction is to stop her. Carmen makes believe she does not see what the bugles have to do with it. Is he tired, perhaps, of seeing her dance without an orchestra to accompany her? And she sings, plays, and dances more vigorously than ever. Again Don José stops her: he has to get back to camp. Now Carmen, like any worthy artist interrupted in a performance—or like any pretty girl whose plans are upset—is really angry.

"Here I've been singing and dancing and, Lord deliver us! I might have loved him pretty soon." (Carmen uses the somewhat cheap device of addressing an imaginary third person.) "Then the bugle sounds—*ta ra ta ta*—and off he goes. All right, get out, you canary," and she takes his soldier's cap, his sword, and his ammunition box and viciously hurls them across the stage at him. Piteously he tells her he does not want to go—he loves her—no other woman has ever touched him so. Carmen only grows angrier and thinks of more insults to shout at him. Thereupon Don José's spirit rises too, and he insists that she listen to him. Finally he gets her quieted down a little and seated in a chair. Then he draws from his vest the flower she had thrown to him in Act I and sings the "Flower Song" (see p. 344), telling her how through all the time he was in prison the flower kept its fragrance and always suggested her to him.*

Though Carmen is obviously moved by this declaration, her first words (after the applause has subsided) are, "No, you don't love me." But this time she speaks far more softly, and her line is quite different. He doesn't love her, she says, for if he did he would follow her up to the free mountains, where there are no officers to be obeyed, where their own will would be their law, where there is liberty. Don José, frantically torn between her invitation and his sense of duty, almost capitulates. He takes her in his arms and is about to kiss her, when his sense of honor makes him push her away. "Go, then!" cries Carmen. "I hate you!" José utters four last passionate adieus and starts to go.

But there is a knock at the door. For a moment the two hesitate, and then Captain Zuniga opens it for himself and enters with a sardonic smile. "Your taste isn't awfully good," he tells Carmen, "taking a plain soldier in preference to an officer," and he orders Don José out. Don José, however, proudly refuses; Zuniga draws his sword, and the two start fighting. Carmen calls for help,† the gypsies pour in from

every side, and Dancaïre and Remendado disarm the Captain. With exquisite politeness, but at the points of two wicked-looking pistols, the Captain is invited to leave the house,

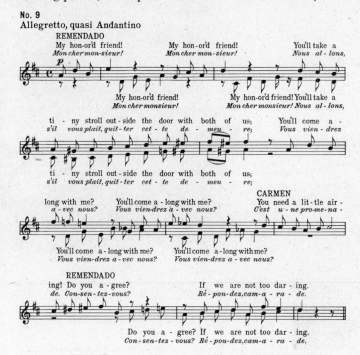

No. 9
Allegretto, quasi Andantino

and with equal Latin polish he admits that their arguments are irresistible.

With the army out of the way, José has no choice left but to join in with the gypsies, and the act ends on a joyous chorus in praise of liberty sung to the same melody that Carmen had used in urging José to join them.

Act Three

THE Prelude to the third act is a charming little piece starting with a flute solo to harp accompaniment, its first two bars bearing an accidental and irrelevant resemblance to "The Minstrel Boy."

No. 10
Andantino, quasi Allegretto

Soon other instruments join in with countermelodies; the first violins sing out, and then there is a long, slow diminuendo. Unlike the preludes to the other acts, it bears no discernible relationship to what is to follow and, as a matter of fact, was originally written as incidental music to the play *L'Arlésienne*.

The curtain rises on a wild spot in the mountains, where the smugglers have gathered their goods in bales preparatory to crossing some unspecified border. They sing a quiet, weird little march, encouraging each other in the dangers that their business presents. Dancaïre, the leader of the smugglers, tells them to rest here for an hour while a small reconnaissance party goes out. As they put down their loads to rest, a short dialogue between Carmen and Don José shows us that their affair has not been going too well. Don José (to a brief quotation from the melody that had accompanied the reading of his letter in Act I) thinks regretfully of how he has disappointed his mother in this new life of his. Carmen, of course, is thoroughly contemptuous of any such softness, and she tells him he'd better go back to Mamma at once.

"And be separated from you?" says Don José, with the

---

*The staging presents an interesting problem in temperament. Carmen, of course, must be impressed by Don José's sincerity and show her growing conviction in pantomime. A first-class actress manages to do this without detracting from the effect of the fine aria; but many insecure prima donnas take so much attention to themselves that they ruin the tenor's big moment. Sometimes they go so far as to start chewing an apple, spitting out the peel, and then laying it down and turning around just as the tenor comes to his high B flat. The B flat, by the way, is marked *pianissimo* but is seldom sung anything softer than *ff*.

†This bit of business, clearly indicated in the libretto, strikes some singers as being so thoroughly out of character that they register a psychologically more probable reaction: Carmen indicates pleasure over having a couple of men in uniform fight for her.

fateful No. 3 playing in the orchestra.

"Of course."

"Carmen, listen," cries Don José warningly. "If you say that again——"

"Then perhaps you'll kill me. So what? It's all a matter of destiny."

Meantime, on one side of the stage, Frasquita and Mercédès have seated themselves before a bale and are busy laying out cards to tell their own fortunes. In a gay, lighthearted duet Frasquita reports that the cards promise her a fine young lover, who takes her on his horse up to the mountains, showers her with attentions, and finally becomes a famous leader of a hundred men. Mercédès has what she apparently thinks an even finer fate in store for her. She is to be wooed by a very rich and very old man who will marry her, present her with diamonds and a castle, and then—oh joy!—die and leave it all to her.

Presently Carmen makes a trio of this duet, spreading out her own pack of cards. Her mood and her music are quite different from her friends'. She lays out a diamond, then a spade, and reads them to mean that she is to die first, then Don José—and she sings a slow, ominous, heavy melody concerning the vanity of trying to avoid death when it is in the cards (see p. 349). Mercédès and Frasquita take up their jollier tune again, while Carmen continues to sing of her dark forebodings.

The "hour" Dancaïre had spoken of is apparently up, for he returns to report that now is the time to pass over. He has seen three customs officers, but he thinks they can be easily handled. Don José is to stay behind to guard what they cannot carry on their first trip.

They all shoulder bales and sing another marchlike tune—this time quite jolly, however, because they are looking forward to the encounter with the customs officers. They're gallant fellows, say the girls, and with a smile, a compliment, and an arm about the waist they should present no danger. Now we know why Dancaïre and Remendado had insisted on having

the girls along. All of them go out, including Don José, who is supposed to mount a height off stage so that he can have a view of the road.

Now Micaëla comes in for her aria—an aria so effective that it often earns more applause than anything the leading lady in the role of Carmen can elicit (see p. 352). Micaëla is frightened almost to death, first by the ominous character of the place but also by the possibility of meeting Carmen, whose wicked allurements have seduced the man she used to love. Desperately Micaëla tries to support her own spirits, but all she can do is to pray to God to protect her. Nor is her courage helped much by seeing Don José up there on his hill aiming with his gun in her general direction. As he fires, she runs out as fast as she can.

It is apparently not Micaëla but Escamillo whom Don José has seen climbing up to the smugglers' rendezvous. The Toreador comes in, dryly remarking that if the shot had been just a little lower, he would have been done for. José challenges him at once, for he knows of him by name only. When Escamillo identifies himself, José welcomes him but tells him he has run quite a risk. "You're telling me," says Escamillo in effect. "But I'm in love, and what fool wouldn't risk his life to see his girl?"

It does not take long for José to find out that it is Carmen whom Escamillo has come to see. The Toreador quite innocently tells his rival that Carmen had had an affair with a soldier who deserted for her, but it's all over now: Carmen's love affairs never last over six months.

"You know, I suppose," says José, scarcely able to contain himself, "that to take our gypsy girls you have to pay in knife thrusts?"

Escamillo understands almost at once that his companion is the deserter himself. He announces that he will be "ravished" to exchange blows with him, and they sing a short duet (one of the less successful passages in the opera) in which José angrily hopes to make Escamillo's blood flow, while Escamillo remarks coolly how amusing it is that he should have come in search of a mistress and run across her lover. The trouble with the music is that the two men—expressing different emotions—sing in like rhythms; and as they are singing simultaneously, the words cannot be followed. Only a reader of the libretto could tell that the two do not feel exactly alike about the coming battle.

They wrap their cloaks about their left arms, draw their knives, and go to it. Escamillo trips, his knife snaps, and José is about to strike him when Carmen, who has heard the noise, grabs hold of his arm. The other gypsies follow close behind and separate the fighters. The Toreador gathers up his dignity with his cloak (he has not for a moment lost his aplomb in the face of death: that is part of his profession) and says that he is "ravished" (one of his favorite words) to have been saved by Carmen. As for Don José, he'll give him a return match any day he wants.

Dancaïre interrupts here and politely tells Escamillo to get out. "Just one more thing," says the Toreador; and he invites everyone present to his next bullfight in Seville, where he promises to perform brilliantly. "Anyone who loves me," he adds, looking directly at Carmen, "will be there." Don José tries to attack him again, but Dancaïre and Remendado hold him back, and Escamillo makes an effective exit to a slow, quiet version of the refrain from the Toreador Song, the contrapuntal harmonization suggesting something more ominous than the brilliantly colored version we had heard in the previous act.

The smugglers are about to go back to their job when one of them discovers Micaëla hiding among the rocks. Don José greets her at once and asks what makes her so mad as to come here. Breaking into the expressive melody of their Act I duet,

she tells him that his mother is weeping and waiting for him, and asks him to take pity on her and come home. Carmen advises him that he'd better go along: gypsying is scarcely his métier. This remark makes Don José furious, and in good, operatic heroics he insists that he will not leave her now. The entire troupe tries to persuade him that he had better, that staying will probably cost him his life. They only make him insist more passionately that he won't leave now, come what will; but Micaëla has one more card to play. She tells him that his mother is dying and wants to see her son once more before death so that she may pardon him. This news changes his mind. After a word of warning to Carmen that he means to return, he is about to leave with Micaëla when the voice of Escamillo, singing his Toreador refrain, comes floating up the mountainside. Carmen starts to run to Escamillo, but José turns back and refuses to let her.

That, in the score, is how the act ends, but imaginative stage managers have invented all sorts of business for the closing ten bars of music. The most common practice on American stages today is to have Carmen struggle violently with Don José to get by, whereupon he throws her to the ground with such force that the prima donna sometimes is really hurt a bit and both get publicity in the newspapers. Another piece of pantomime sometimes used is to have Carmen attack Don José with a knife, whereupon he bears his breast to receive it, and she shrinks back from actual murder. This makes an effective curtain, but it is scarcely in character for Carmen to shrink from any violence. At any rate, Bizet apparently never considered any such business, for the closing music is—with the exception of four quick chords at the end— a quiet, uneventful diminuendo.

Act Four

THE Entr'acte that precedes Act IV opens with a brief burst of vigorous Spanish dance rhythm and then subsides into a winding, attractive melody said to be based on a genuine Andalusian song and dance, the *polo*.

No. 11
Allegro

It makes an admirable preface to the ballet that follows— or follows, at least, when the opera company possesses a ballet group it likes to show off, for the dancing in the final act is optional in the score.

The scene is the square in Seville outside an ancient amphitheater where, as posters tell us, a bullfight is to be held that day. Fan girls, orange girls, program, cigarette, and water peddlers mix in among the soldiers and the citizens who are

waiting outside to watch the expected procession of performers and officials into the amphitheater. There are holiday bustle, noisy, rhythmic Spanish music, and (optionally) a ballet danced to music by Bizet, usually borrowed from *L'Arlésienne*. Then the procession starts to music that we have already heard in the Prelude to the opera. First come the various functionaries and assistants and finally the matador himself.* He, of course, is Escamillo, and on his arm is Carmen

---

*The order of the procession is carefully indicated in the score, each group in turn enthusiastically greeted by the crowd. First comes the local constabulary; then the *chulos*, a group of footmen provided with crimson banners to take off the attention of the bull after one or more horses or men have been wounded; then the *banderilleros*, men with sharp-barbed darts who worry the bull after the *picadors* are through; then the *cuadrilla*, which is a sort of matador's fan club; then the *picadors*, horsemen with lances, who excite the bull before the matador engages him; and then the *matador*. Escamillo is always referred to as a *toreador*; but as a *toreador* is generally supposed to ride a horse, the term *matador* is a little more accurate. Few opera houses are willing to risk their star baritone's dignity and neck on a ride across the stage.

dressed in all the finery he can afford. The crowd, which has joyfully greeted each of the other functionaries and groups, bursts into the chorus of the Toreador Song for him.

There is a brief, sentimental duet between Escamillo and Carmen, in which he tells her that if she loves him she can now be proud of him, while she replies that she certainly does love him—may she die if she has ever loved anyone so much!

While the chief magistrate of Seville—the alcalde—and his guards enter the amphitheater in back, Frasquita and Mercédès take Carmen aside to warn her that Don José is hiding in the crowd and that she had better be careful. Carmen sees him, but says that she is not afraid of him—in fact, she will wait and talk to him right here.

The bright A-major theme of the Prelude (No. 1) fades into a *pianissimo* as Frasquita and Mercédès follow the crowd into the amphitheater, and then a crescendo rumbling and a loud chord usher in Don José, wretchedly dressed in a torn, pale-yellow shirt.

"I've just heard," says Carmen, "that you were around and that I'd better look out for my life. But I'm not afraid—I won't run."

Don José, however, is here only to plead, he says, not to threaten, and he begs her to go away with him. "Impossible," says Carmen, lapsing into the third person again. "Carmen never lies; her spirit is inflexible; all is over." Passionately

Don José tries to move that spirit, nevertheless—he will do anything, even turn brigand again for her; but the more he pleads, the more Carmen scorns him. When the *vivas* hailing Escamillo are heard, she brightens and tries to enter the amphitheater, but Don José blocks the way and demands whether she loves the Toreador. "Yes, I love him," she shouts, "and even in the face of death, I'll repeat it: I love him!"

Now the orchestra tears out the fateful theme No. 3, and Don José swears that he cannot bear her laughing at him in Escamillo's arms. Once more he demands that she come with him, but Carmen cries angrily, "Kill me now, or let me pass." Again a shout of "Victory" comes from the amphitheater; and Carmen tears a ring from her finger that José had once given her and hurls it away.

Then, while the crowd inside is singing the chorus of the Toreador Song in praise of the victorious Escamillo, Carmen tries to elude Don José and rush into the amphitheater, but he quickly draws his knife, grasps hold of her, and plunges it in. The crowd, coming from the theater, finds him on his knees beside her body.

"You can arrest me. I killed her," he says brokenly; and then bursts out sobbing, "Oh! Carmen, my adored Carmen——!"

The orchestra finishes the broken phrase for him as the curtain comes down.

Habanera

portamento

plan, Some may woo him with rhymes and ver-ses, Give me a strong and si-lent man.___
tait; Et c'est l'au-tre que je pré-fè-re Il n'a rien dit;___mais_il me plait.

espressivo

Ah, love!___ Ah, love!___
La - mour!___ La - mour!___

Chorus

Gyp-sy love is a rov-ing rap-ture, A wan-ton bird that none can tame, Not a
L'a-mour est un oi-seau re-bel-le Que nul ne peut ap-pri-voi-ser, Et c'est

pp

Ah, love!___ Ah, love! Oh, love is
l'a - mour!___ l'a - mour! L'a-mour est

bird for a fool to cap-ture, He plays a most e-lu-sive game.
bien en vain qu'on l'ap-pel-le S'il lui con-vient de___re-fu-ser.

p

just a gyp-sy lad, He nev - er could and nev - er would play fair, So if you
en - fant de Bo - hême, il n'a ja - mais, ja-mais con - nu de loi, Si tu ne

Cho: You must be -
Prends garde à

turn from me, I'll love — you, But if I do, why then take care! _____
m'ai - mes pas, je t'ai - me; Si je t'ai - me, prends garde à toi! _____

f

Cho: You must be -
Prends garde a

ware!
toi!

So if you turn from me, If you re - fuse my love I'll love you,
Si tu ne m'ai - mes pas, si tu ne m'ai-mes pas, je t'ai - me!

pp

f

ware!
toi! *cresc.*

But if I love you, If I love _ you, Why then be - ware! _____
Mais si je t'ai - me, si je t'ai - me, prends gar - de à toi! _____

p *cresc.* *f*

ff

Say to My José
ET TU LUI DIRAS

Original key: B-flat

Say to my Jo - sé when you find him, That his
Et tu lui di - ras que sa mè - re Son - ge

moth - er sends a fond em - brace;
nuit et jour à l'ab - sent,

Say I for - give him and re - mind him, How I have
Qu'el - le re - grette et qu'elle es - pè - re, Qu'el - le par -

longed to see his face. Find my
don - ne et quel - le at - tend. Tout ce -

Seguidilla

Allegretto

CARMEN

There's a ca - fé in Sé - vil - - la,
Près des rem - parts de Sé - vil - - le,

Kept by my friend Lil - las Pas - tia, Where
Chez mon a - mi Lil - las Pas - tia, J'i -

I dance a smooth Sé - gue - dil - la and drink Man - za -
rai dan - ser la Sé - gue - dille Et boi - re du Man - za -

nil - la. _____ I will soon be there with Lil - las
nil - la. _____ J'i - rai chez mon a - mi Lil - las

Pas - tia. _____
Pas - tia. _____

sempre pp

legato

Ped.

threw him out the oth-er day! Now__ my poor heart
l'ai mis à la por-te hier! *Mon__ pau-vre cœur*

looks for a lov- er, Free__ for what- ev - er
très con - so - la - ble, *Mon__ cœur est li - bre*

comes__ its way; I could have had a score of men,__
com - me l'air, *J'ai des ga - lants à la dou-zai - ne,*

But none has set my heart a-whirl, And still I hope for some-thing more of men, Are
Mais ils ne sont pas à mon gré, *Voi - ci la fin de la se - mai - ne; Qui*

town of Se-vil - - la, Down to my
parts de Sé - vil - - le, Chez mon a-

friend Lil-las Pas - tia; The danc-ing is
mi Lil-las Pas - tia, J'i-rai dan-ser

fine and the mu-sic is di - vine in Se-vil-la,
la Sé-gue-dille Et boi-re du Man-za-nil-la.

Tra-la la la la la la la la la la la!

Toreador Song

VOTRE TOAST

Allegro molto moderato

Original key

play without Ped

ESCAMILLO

f ben ritmato

Here's a **toast** to Spain's mighty he- - roes, To

Vo- tre toast, je peux vous le ren- - dre, Se-

you, sen - ors,___ who keep her hon - or bright,___
ñors, se - ñors,___ car a - vec les sol - dats___

Some men are sol - diers, Some are Tor - ér - os
Oui, les To - ré - ros, peu - vent s'en - ten - dre;

What's it mat - ter what we are, We all love_ a fight.___
Pour plai - sirs,___ pour plai - sirs, ils ont les _ com - bats! ___

On a hol - i - day, the stands are teem - ing With
Le __ cir - que est plein, c'est jour de fê - - te! Le

men and wom - - en,_ girls and boys,_
cirque est plein _ du _ haut en bas; _

How they are shout - ing, stamp - ing and scream - ing,
Les spec - ta - teurs, _ per - dant la tê - te,

In they go to see the show and make a glo - ri - ous noise!_
Les _ spec - ta - teurs s'in - ter - pel - lent à grand fra - cas! _

Some are cheer - ing and some are jeer - ing,_ Some_ rave_ and roar with
A - pos - tro - phes, cris et ta - pa - ge Pous - sés _ jus - ques à

all their might.___ Now the brave___ Tor-ér-o
la fu - reur!___ Car___ c'est___ la fê - te

is ap-pear - - ing, Hear the crowd cheer-ing at the
du cou - ra - - ge! C'est la fê - te des gens de

sight, On guard, hold stead-y, Come on, Come
cœur! Al - lons! en gar - de! al - lons! al -

on!___ Ah!___
lons!___ ah!___

Son of Alcala

HALTE-LÀ!

Allegro moderato

Original key: G minor

Carmen's Song and Dance

Flower Song
FAITES-LUI MES AVEUX

Original key: C

fra - grance still re - mained. Through the hours I spent there with-
jours_____ sa douce o - deur; Et pen - dant des heu - res en-

out you, It would set me dream-ing a - bout. you; Its
tiè - res, Sur mes yeux, fer - mant mes pau - piè - res, De

sweet per - fume_ would fill the air, And I would see you_ be-side me
cette o - deur je m'e - ni - vrais Et dans la nuit_____ je te vo-

Poco animato, ma poco cresc.

there._____ I cursed the day_ when first I met you, I
yais!_____ Je me pre - nais_ à te mau - di - re, A

dim.

pp

sempre ben legato

) 345 (

tried to des-pise, to for-get you; I asked my-self why this should
te dé-tes-ter, à me di-re: Pour-quoi faut-il que le des-

be, ___ Why fate's de-cree ___ led you to me! ___ Then
tin ___ L'ait_ mi-se là ___ sur mon che-min! ___ Puis

I broke the spell that op-pressed me, And there came a dream that pos-
je m'ac-cu-sais de blas-phè-me, Et je ne sen-tais en moi-

sessed me, My on-ly hope, ___ my on-ly goal, The on-ly
mê-me, Je ne sen-tais ___ qu'un seul dé-sir, un seul dé-

wor - ship and a - dore you; Oh, my Car - men,
rer de tout mon ê tre, Ô ma Car - men!

Here at your feet I lay my heart!
Et j'é - tais u - ne chose à toi!

Car - men, I love you!
Car - men, je t'ai - - me!

Card Song

EN VAIN POUR ÉVITER

) 349 (

gay,   The cards re - veal it so: Your card will come to
reu - se, Mêle et cou - pe sans peur: La car - te sous tes

poco sf

hand in some mys - ter - ious   way,   And you will   deal it so! ___
doigts se tour - ne - ra joy - euse,   T'an-non-cant   le bon - heur! ___

But if you're doomed to   die, Ac-cept the sad de - cree,   And save your
Mais si tu dois mou - rir, Si le mot re-dou - ta - ble   Est è - crit

poco cresc.

fee - ble breath; ___   Oh, cut them as you   like, Your card is sure to
par le sort, ___   Re - com-mence vingt fois,   la car - te im - pi - to -

poco cresc.

Micaela's Aria
JE DIS, QUE RIEN NE M'ÉPOUVANTE

Original key: E-flat

Andante molto

MICAELA

say _____ that I'm not a - fraid, _____ I ___ speak, a -
dis, _____ que rien ne m'é-pou - van - - te, Je dis,_ hé -

las, on - ly to hide_ my fear; Though I pre -
las! que je ré - ponds_ de moi; Mais j'ai beau

tend _____ that I'm not dis - mayed, _____ I feel in my
fai - re la_vail - lan - te, Au fond_ du

heart _____ there's dan - ger near!
coeur _____ je_ meurs d'ef - froi!

un poco meno p

Here, _____ in this lone - ly place, _____ I am froz - en with
Seu - - le en ce lieu - sau - va - ge, Tou - te seu - le j'ai

cresc. molto

fear _____ al-though to fear is wrong! _____
peur, _____ mais j'ai tort d'a - voir peur; _____

cresc.

R.H.

) 353 (

Gra - cious Lord, Keep me safe and pro-
O Sei - gneur! don - nez - moi du cou-

tect me! Be thou my shield,
ra - ge! Pro - tè - gez - moi!

Thou, my sword, Be thou my strength,
O Sei - gneur! pro - tè - gez - moi!

O
Sei -

Lord!
gneur!

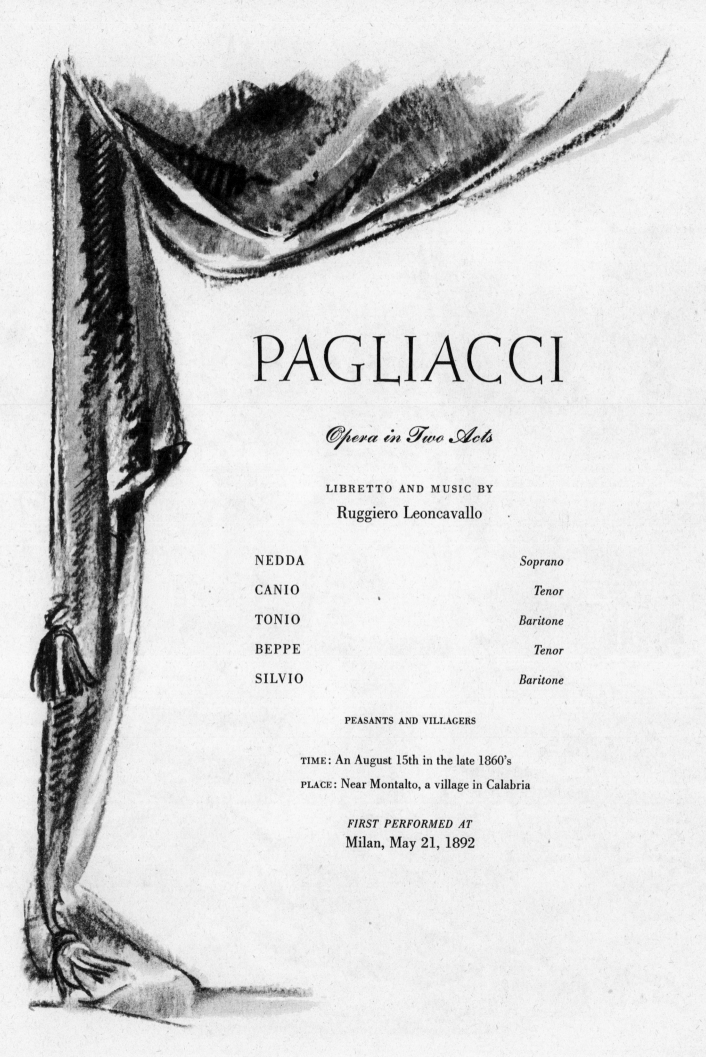

PAGLIACCI

Opera in Two Acts

LIBRETTO AND MUSIC BY
Ruggiero Leoncavallo

NEDDA	*Soprano*
CANIO	*Tenor*
TONIO	*Baritone*
BEPPE	*Tenor*
SILVIO	*Baritone*

PEASANTS AND VILLAGERS

TIME: An August 15th in the late 1860's

PLACE: Near Montalto, a village in Calabria

FIRST PERFORMED AT
Milan, May 21, 1892

Pagliacci

RUGGIERO LEONCAVALLO

THERE are some striking parallels in the histories of *Pagliacci* and its perennial teammate, *Cavallerria Rusticana*. Both were the works of young, unknown composers eking out wretched lives with hack work. Each achieved an early reputation and lifelong affluence for its creator. Neither composer was ever again able remotely to equal the initial success. Both operas were published by the firm of Sonzogno. Both operas are, of course, examples par excellence of what is called "verism," and as such both have been repeatedly scorned by critics, particularly German critics and others who look to Germany for critical principles. Despite all the vilification, they have both remained enormously popular, and in Germany itself in the year 1938 (the last year for which figures are available) *Pagliacci* was performed more often than any other grand opera. There it is called *Bajazzo*.

Pagliacci, as a matter of fact, was directly inspired by the success of *Cavalleria*, which had won a prize from Sonzogno in a competition for one-act operas. Leoncavallo, the son of a circuit judge, had been something of a prodigy. At sixteen he had been graduated from the Naples Conservatory; at twenty he had earned the degree of doctor of letters from the University of Bologna. Like Wagner, he considered himself just as much a man of letters as a musician, and he wrote the librettos for most of his own works. On one occasion he said that he did not see how one could set anyone else's words successfully—a remark aimed, apparently, at his rivals Mascagni and Puccini, for he must have forgotten the example of the revered Verdi when he made it.

Leoncavallo's double talent, however, had not enabled him to make a good living. He had tried his hand at accompanying, at being a pianist in Egypt (where he had had to leave rather hurriedly), at operatic coaching. None afforded him a successful livelihood, and for a time he had even been a café pianist. He had great ambitions, however, and got the publisher Ricordi to listen to him read *I Medici*, the first work in a never-completed trilogy meant to glorify the Italian Renais-sance, just as Wagner had glorified Teutonic mythology. Ricordi offered him twenty-four hundred francs to compose the music, which he did within a year; but this opera never saw the stage till after the success of *Pagliacci*, and then it was a failure.

So Leoncavallo went back to coaching opera singers till Mascagni had his great success, when he decided on one more try. He wrote the book and composed the music for *Pagliacci* in the space of five months, and Sonzogno accepted it for both publication and production after reading only the libretto. Maybe the offer of the great baritone Victor Maurel, a friend of Leoncavallo's, to create the role of Tonio had something to do with the speedy acceptance. It was produced first at the Teatro dal Verme in Milan on May 21, 1892, when Leoncavallo was thirty-four, and it was an immediate and enormous success. That was just two years and four days after the *première* of its teammate, *Cavalleria Rusticana*, in Rome.

The central dramatic idea of *Pagliacci*—the play-within-a-play during which a real murder of revenge is committed—is at least as old as Thomas Kyd's sixteenth-century *Spanish Tragedie*. As it happens, Leoncavallo's story is, according to his own account, based on an actual case tried before his father in Calabria, where the opera is laid. The Canio of real life (whose name was Alessandro) exclaimed after the trial that he'd do it all over again if he had to. Thereupon he received a prison sentence for his double murder, on the expiration of which he became a domestic in the household of a Baroness Sproniere.

The success of the opera was so great that the French dramatist Catulle Mendès threatened suit for plagiarism because his play, *La Femme de Tabarin*, with incidental music by Chabrier, had used a similar dramatic device five years earlier. Leoncavallo pointed to a still older play by the Spanish dramatist Estebanez that had used this device, and then told the story of the genesis of his opera (which is based on a play he had written even earlier). Mendès withdrew.

Given the crude, violent, elemental emotions of this

story of peasant love and hate, it is difficult to understand the hoity-toity criticism leveled at the opera. The libretto is a little masterpiece of concise, clear storytelling. With the exception of the "Bell Chorus," there is scarcely a line which does not contribute to the painting of character or the advancement of the plot. Even this chorus may be excused on the ground that it denotes the passing of time, while Leoncavallo used to defend it for being a piece of genuine local color.

The music is vigorous and broadly colored, the use of specific themes for specific emotions transparently obvious (though not so obvious that any commentary I have read has succeeded in pointing out all of them). To tell this sort of tale, this is the right sort of music. What do the critics want? Debussyan pastels? Wagnerian grandeur? Gluck's nobility or Mozart's sweetness? *Pagliacci* is all of a piece, a sure dramatic blow between the eyes. The opera public of every country has found it so and therefore given it the ultimate accolade of paying over and over again to hear it. That, in the last analysis—according to both Verdi and Leoncavallo—is the one true test of the merit of an opera.

Prologue

BEFORE the famous baritone solo known as *the* Prologue, the orchestra has a prelude of its own which sets forth the four principal musical themes of the opera. They are not exactly leitmotivs in the Wagnerian sense because they are not so fully developed and transformed. Yet they are frequently used throughout with dramatic effect.

The lively, opening theme is associated with the strolling players as a group, the *pagliacci*.*

No. 1
Vivace

The rhythm of the first bar forms the basis of most of the orchestral prelude, but the note of liveliness is interrupted briefly to introduce the other three themes in this order:

No. 2
Largo

This, played by a quartet of French horns, is used at the climax of the famous "*Ridi, pagliaccio*" aria and again at the very close of the opera in connection with Canio's utter despair. It is followed by

No. 3
Andante cantabile

Sung out by the violins, this can be called the love theme of the opera, and it subsides into the low strings giving out *mis-*

*The word "*pagliacci*" means literally "chopped straws," referring to the straws which strolling players wore in their hats.

terioso, the theme used for Canio's suspicions and jealousy:

No. 4
Misterioso

The *pagliacci* theme is picked up again, worked up to a heated climax; there is a sudden rest; the sixteenth notes of the theme are repeated twice, like a question, and the clown, Tonio, sticks his head through the curtain. With mock modesty he asks whether he may not have a word with the audience. The author of the play, it seems, has revived the old-fashioned prologue to be addressed directly to the audience. Only, says Tonio, there's this difference: once upon a time the prologue used to say that stage passions are not anything to take seriously or become alarmed at. Quite the contrary. *This* show is going to be a bleeding shred of reality. Love, hate, and despair all will be depicted—and the orchestra uses Nos. 2, 4, and 3. The story to be unfolded is a memory of something that really happened, and no one must forget that under the poor costumes breathe men of flesh and bone. Tonio sings this last part to a broadly sweeping melody, later used for the Intermezzo between the acts. Almost invariably the singer interpolates a high A flat toward the end—or at least an F. Then he subsides, almost into speech, and says, "Well, that's the idea. Let's begin." And after an interpolated high G (a D in the score), he disappears again while applause drowns out the orchestra's coda based on No. 1† (see p. 367).

†It has been Lawrence Tibbett's habit to sing the Prologue without Tonio's traditional red wig, only half made up, and walking erect instead of with the traditional slouch or hunchback the misshapen character is supposed to have. Other baritones have tried delivering the Prologue in formal evening attire. The effect is good, but it means some very rapid make-up and costume changing, for Tonio is supposed to be on the stage when the curtain rises and can at best delay putting in an appearance for two or three minutes.

Act One

THE scene of the opera is at the meeting of two roads outside a village in Calabria, the province of Italy that covers the forefoot of the Italian map. The year is specified as in the late 1860's, the date as August 15, the Feast of the Assumption. It is 3 P. M. and a bright, sunny afternoon.

Even before the curtain goes up, we hear a discordant trumpet with bass drums and cymbals announcing the arrival of the strolling players. A crowd of villagers dressed for the holiday has gathered at the crossroads to greet them, considerable noise and life being added to the excitement by a group of unruly boys. The misshapen misanthrope, Tonio, has arrived ahead of the rest of the troupe and, annoyed by the stares of the crowd, lies down in the shade of the impromptu stage that has been set up for the evening's performance. Off stage, above the hubbub, are heard the voices of the leader of the troupe, Canio, and its juvenile lead, Beppe. They are clearing the road for their entrance in a cart drawn by a small donkey. The cart is occupied by a big bass drum, Canio, and Nedda, his wife and leading lady. Canio, in the traditional Punchinello costume, is apparently a popular figure. He beats the drum loudly and elicits bravos with a few grimaces and such side-splitting jokes as "Thank you!" Finally he gets everyone's undivided attention and outlines the general plot of the play to be presented that evening, ending up with an attractive little waltz tune that the crowd repeats after him:*

It should be remembered, to understand fully the events of the second act, that the Punch-and-Judy plot of the play was traditional in its general outlines and that it was the custom of strolling players to improvise their lines on an agreed-upon scenario rather than to memorize a printed play. Many strolling players were illiterates.

As Canio descends from the cart, he finds Tonio offering to help Nedda off and hits him on the head. The crowd thinks this a charming bit of comedy, but Tonio takes it in very bad part and goes into the theater cursing his master and threatening revenge. A moment later a couple of villagers invite the players to go into town for a drink. Tonio, who is rubbing down the donkey that Beppe has led off, says he will follow along after the others, and one of the villagers jokingly warns Canio that Tonio may be staying behind only to pay court to Nedda. Canio does not think that a very funny joke, as he explains dramatically to the surprised villagers in the short aria "*Un tal gioco*" (see p. 377). Canio's character of professional leading man is admirably set forth in the music—much more clearly than in the more famous "*Vesti la giubba.*" Knitting his brows, he takes the villager by the arm and—when he is sure he has his undivided attention—tells him quietly and earnestly that neither Tonio nor anyone else had better try anything of the sort. Then, acting out the part, he says that it is all well enough up there on the stage to act the easygoing husband for the sake of applause. But off the stage, that's another matter—and here the music works up to a climax on No. 4, the theme associated with Canio's suspicion and jealousy. Then he repeats his quiet and earnest warning, and Nedda,

No. 5
Vivo

Dear la - dies and gen - tle-men, our show __ will be - giv - en
Ve - ni - te, o-no - ra - te - ci, si - gno - ri e si - gno - re!

This ev-ning at sev - en, this ev-ning at sev - en!
A ven-ti-trè o - re! a ven-ti-trè o - re!

*The Italian phrase "*a venti-tre ore*" translated literally means "at twenty-three o'clock." In some parts of Italy, time was counted from 8 P.M. on. Thus 9 P.M. was one o'clock and 7 P.M. became twenty-three o'clock.

overhearing him from the other side of the stage, shudders. The villagers refuse to take all this seriously; and Canio, to dispel the momentary cloud that has come over the happy day, laughs it off and runs across the stage to kiss Nedda with underscored fondness.

For no particular reason, except perhaps that Leoncavallo thought he must insert one set chorus number, a group of bagpipers crosses the back of the stage and reminds the villagers that church is about to begin. Canio sticks his head through the curtains of the theater to repeat his invitation to the show and—usually—to deliver himself of a high B that is not in the score. The charming "Bell Chorus" follows, with its attractive harmonic progression toward the end:

No. 6
Andantino

and the crowd files out.

Nedda is left alone on the stage, still shaken by Canio's exhibition of unfounded jealous rage. "Suppose he should really discover my secret thoughts," she mutters to herself—and the love and jealousy themes suggest to us that Canio may after all have reason for doubting his wife's faithfulness.

But it is too fine a day and Nedda is too full of life to be long detained by such gloomy thoughts. With the fiddles trilling high up, she gazes up at the skies and sings to the birds a happy, carefree aria, the Balatella, or "Bird Song" (see p. 381). Meanwhile, Tonio sidles in, sits down beside the stage, and when she is through joins the audience in applauding—only his applause is tinged with mockery. Nedda, who obviously hasn't much use for the company clown, speaks sharply to him and tells him to get out and join the others in their drinking.

Tonio, however, is serious in his love-making. He may be horrible to look at, deformed as he is, but he says that he cannot help loving her. It is a melodically eloquent plea, but Nedda only laughs at him. To a light, joking melody in the orchestra

No. 7
Scherzoso con eleganza

she tells him to save his love-making for the show that evening (In the second act, when the play itself is on, this same melody appears in a parallel situation.) Still Tonio is not to be put off. His wooing becomes more violent as Nedda's scorn mounts. Finally he attempts to force her to kiss him, whereupon she takes up a whip and strikes viciously at her tormentor. Cowering before the weapon, Tonio screams a curse at her. By the Virgin of the fifteenth of August (the Feast of the Assumption, the day of the happenings), he swears he will even things with her, while the orchestra plays an ominous series of notes:

No. 8
Moderato

And as he hobbles off, she sends one more insult in his direction. His spirit, she says, is as misshapen as his body and as dirty too.

Hardly has Tonio departed by the rear left exit, when a handsome young villager named Silvio hops over a low wall on the right. He is announced in the orchestra by the love theme (No. 3), and a large part of the long love duet that follows is based on the same melody and variations of it (see p. 389). Silvio, the dialogue tells us, has taken advantage of the other men's drinking at the tavern to sneak around for a daylight visit with Nedda. He almost ran into Tonio, says Nedda, and she tells him of her unpleasant encounter with the clown. That sort of thing, apparently, is only one of the aspects of the life of a strolling player she does not like. Her husband is another. Silvio urges her to elope with him, and her initial refusals, though passionately expressed, are never entirely convincing, as she always insists that she loves only Silvio and will entrust herself entirely to him. Finally, as they recall the kisses they have enjoyed on some other unspecified occasion, their voices rise together, and she succumbs.

During one of their passionate exchanges during the early part of the duet (which, by the way, is usually cut by forty-five bars as being too long), Tonio passes across the back of the stage. As the double basses growl out the same dramatic intervals that had accompanied Tonio's earlier defeat (No. 8), he gloats over this chance for revenge.

The same theme accompanies Tonio as he leads Canio on at the back of the stage just as the lovers bid farewell. They are around the corner of the improvised stage, and Canio just has time to hear his wife arrange to meet her lover that very night after the performance, but not to see who the lover is. For as Canio bursts away from Tonio's restraining hands, Silvio jumps over the wall. Canio chases off stage after him, having first to push Nedda out of the way, and Tonio rubs his hands with satisfaction and gloats over the way he is paying back his debt. Pretty soon, he says, he hopes to do even better.

Unable to find Silvio because the villager knows the paths better, Canio returns almost at once and demands to know who it was; for if he has not yet slain his wife, he says, it is only because he must first have the name. The orchestra pants out notes from No. 4, the theme of jealousy and suspicion; and when Nedda vigorously refuses to give in to his threats, he draws out a huge knife and runs directly at her, much to Tonio's delight. It is only Beppe's chance return at this moment that saves Nedda. The young man holds back his master, tells him the church is just emptying and people are on their way here, leads Nedda back into the theater, and persuades Tonio to soothe the enraged husband. This Tonio does by picking up the knife from the ground, putting it back into Canio's hands and suggesting that the lover may show up at tonight's performance and give himself away.

When Beppe comes back and leads Tonio off to get ready for the play, Canio is left alone for his big scene—the laugh-clown-laugh aria (see p. 395). It is, perhaps, the most sure-fire scene for solo tenor in any opera, and applause almost invariably interrupts the closing pantomime, in which Canio tries to enter the stage, is overcome by a fit of sobbing, and finally either forces himself to go in or falls down before the curtain in utter despair. So effective, in fact, is this scene that tenors usually take solo bows for a long time after it, the soprano, the two baritones and the secondary tenor having to wait for the close of the second act before they are acknowledged.

Act Two

BEFORE the curtain rises on the second act, there is an orchestral Intermezzo based chiefly on the Prologue. After two sadly dramatic phrases, the violins sing the tune to which Tonio has told us how the story came one morning to the author; and then the whole orchestra sweeps broadly into the final melody of the Prologue, where we are reminded that actors too are men of flesh and blood. To this tune, the cellos play a countermelody that starts with the opening of Canio's great aria; and the Intermezzo closes with the same succession of notes that had closed Act I.

As in the first act, we hear an odd trumpet call and bass-drum notes even before the curtain goes up, and a moment later the gathering of the villagers begins. There is considerable pleasant and tuneful excitement while the audience is filing in for the evening's entertainment. Tonio busily and good-naturedly directs the unruly traffic, and presently Beppe and Nedda come out to help him collect the admission fees. While they are doing this, Silvio finds his seat too and takes the opportunity for a whispered word with his love.

Meantime, the crowd becomes more and more excited, more and more impatient for the performance to begin; and when a loud bell within the theater promises the rising of the curtain, they demand silence of each other with a characteristically Latin *fortissimo*.

In every way, the play-within-a-play is designed to contrast the outward artificialities of the stage with the realities of life that are destined to break it up in the end. The setting is a tiny room with two doors so close to each other that they are obviously there for dramatic purposes only. There is also a convenient window between them. The names of the characters and their costumes are also strictly conventional theater art. Nedda is Columbine, Beppe is Harlequin, Tonio is Taddeo, and Canio is Pagliaccio (or Punchinello). The movements of the actors are also conventionalized, Nedda dancing as often as she walks. As for the music, it is based on dance and opera conventions up to the point where Canio breaks out of the forms of the theatre into the realities of a passionate life.

The opening music of the play-within-a-play is a minuet:

No. 9
Tempo di minuetto

Nedda, as Columbine, is waiting for Taddeo (Tonio) to bring refreshments for a tryst with her lover, for her husband, as she tells us, is not expected till late.

Suddenly we hear a guitar tuning up off stage as Harlequin

(Beppe, of course) prepares to sing a charming, formal serenade to his love (see p. 398). Nedda is enraptured and, to the minuet music (No. 9), prepares to signal her lover. Just then Taddeo comes in and, with a mock operatic cadenza, exclaims how beautiful Columbine is. (Laughter from the stage audience.) And while Nedda takes the chicken he has brought with him and asks how much it cost, Taddeo begins to make love to her, just as he had done as Tonio that afternoon. The orchestra appropriately here plays No. 7, the light melody to which Nedda had told him that he should save his love-making for the play itself. Tonio's pleading again becomes more earnest, and it is stopped only when Harlequin climbs in through the window, deposits a bottle of wine, and gives the clown a good kick in his broad trousers. (More laughter from the stage audience.) Immediately Taddeo rises from his knees, blesses the two lovers, and promises to wait by the door to warn them should Pagliaccio come home.

The two lovers set out their little feast on the table and, as they dance a gavotte, congratulate each other on their joint prospect of love and refreshments (see p. 402). In addition, Harlequin gives Columbine a sleeping draught to be administered to Pagliaccio so that they may elope that evening. Their plot is interrupted at this point by Taddeo, who enters in mock alarm to warn them that Pagliaccio is coming up in a terrific rage. Quickly Harlequin climbs out of the window, and Pagliaccio enters just in time to hear Columbine's final words to her lover: "Till tonight, and I shall be yours forever." These, as Canio mutters to himself, are precisely the words he had heard his wife speak to her lover that afternoon. But he attempts anyway to go on with the actor's part assigned to him, the music being a sad, slightly drunken little tune in minor:

No. 10
Andantino

He accuses her of harboring a lover, pointing out the two places laid for supper; but Columbine says it was only Taddeo, and she opens the left-hand door to reveal the clown. "Believe her, believe her," stutters Tonio, and adds with exaggerated irony, "those faithful lips would hate to utter a lie."

For the moment Canio forgets he is an actor, and to the suspicion-jealousy theme (No. 4) demands her lover's name. Nedda becomes half frightened by this obvious earnestness and attempts to bring Canio back to play-acting by saying lightly, "Pagliaccio, Pagliaccio," while the orchestra plays No. 10.

But now Canio throws aside all pretense at carrying on the plot of the play in formal fashion. Tearing his Punchinello cap from his head, he wipes the grease and powder from his face and bursts into his third aria. "No, Pagliaccio no longer." Passionately he declares he will defend his honor against the cursed woman he had saved from starvation when he first found and then married her. The stage audience thinks this a splendid piece of acting, though a few of the third sopranos —and Silvio—begin to suspect that there is more than a stage play going on before their eyes. Falling into a chair, Canio sings a broad melody telling how he had built all his hopes on Nedda, and works up his passion to a terrible curse on a high B flat. "Bravo!" cries the audience.

Nedda takes it with forced calm. "All right then," she says, "why don't you send me away?" But it would be no salve to Canio's hurt honor to have her go off with her lover. Despite Nedda's determined efforts to resume the tone of the comedy with the melody of the gavotte, Canio insists on knowing the name of the lover. "The name, the name!" he shouts, and Nedda, now also giving up the comedy tone, swears she will never tell him. Beppe appears at the back of the stage and sees that it is time to intercede once more, but this time Tonio holds him back; and with the audience half out of its seats with excitement, Canio draws his large knife, seizes on Nedda, and stabs her twice. "You'll call the name in your death spasm!" he shouts—and as she falls dying, she calls on Silvio for help.

With drawn knife her lover rushes up to the stage, but he is too late. Canio turns on him, stabs him to the heart, and then, turning in stupefaction to the audience, lets fall his bloody weapon as he utters the famous last, spoken line of the opera: "The comedy is over!"

Rapidly the curtain falls as the orchestra blares out No. 2, the laugh-clown-laugh theme.

Prologue

SI PUÒ?

TONIO *(sticking his head through the curtain)*

What ho!
Si può?...

What ho!
Si può?...

Dear
Si -

broadly (bowing)

la - dies and gen - tle-men,
gno - re!... Si - gno - ri!...

You'll bear with me
Scu - sa - te - mi

if I come here be-
se da sol mi pre-

No! The au-thor pre - fers his play to por-tray for you
No. L'au - to - re_ha cer - ca - to in - ve - ce pin - ger - vi

life as all of us know it.
u - no squar - cio di vi - ta.

pause Decisively

Sure - ly the
E - gli_ha per

art - ist should be a - bove all, a man!_____
mas - si - ma sol che l'ar - ti - sta_è_un uom_____

mp (less fast)

All that he writes is for man's un - der - stand - ing,
e che per gli_uo - mi - ni scri - ve - re_ei de - ve.

Jokes Like That One
UN TAL GIOCO

Original key: F

Slowly and very meaningfully

Jokes like that one, I'm warn-ing you,___ it's bet-ter to for-
Un tal gio - co, cre - de - te - mi,___ è me-glio non gio-

get them, My jest - ing broth - er and To - nio, per-haps you
car - lo con me, miei ca - ri; e a To - nio— e un po-co a

might re - gret them! For the art - ist is
tut - ti or par - lo! Il te - a - tro e la

In a livelier mood

one thing, the man is quite an - oth - er;
vi - - ta non son la stes - sa co - sa;

Go, my friends, do not con - fuse them.
no — non son la stes - sa co - sa!

Our play will show Pa - gliac - cio, his
E se las - sù Pa - gliac - cio sor -

la - dy and her lov - er; And
pren - de la sua spo - sa col

when he finds they're fool - ing him, his rage is boil - ing
bel ga - lan - te in ca - me - ra, fa un co - mi - co ser -

o - ver. Then he's qui - et, he sub - sides when his be -
mo - ne, poi si cal - ma od ar - ren - de - si ai

rit.   (clapping his hands)

tray - er wants to beat him! How the au - dience will laugh and ap-plaud when they mis -
col - pi di bas - to - ne! Ed il pub - bli - co ap - plau - de, ri - den - do al - le - gra -

rit.

(Slowly working up a heated passion)
mf

treat him! But if Ned - da should real - ly take a lov - er,
men - te! Ma se Ned - da sul se - rio sor - pren - des - si

mf l.h.

espr.

Then the sto - - - ry would real - tra - men - - - te fi - ni -

quire a trag - ic end - ing and it would not be pre-
reb - - be la sto - ria, co - m'è ver che vi

Tempo Iº *(resuming his quiet, meaningful tone)*

tend - ing!
par - lo!

Jokes like that one, I'm warn - ing you.
Un tal gio - co, cre - de - te - mi,

cresc. molto

May have a trag - ic end - ing.
è me-glio non gio - car - lo!

Bird Song

STRIDONO LASSÙ

Original key: F-sharp

NEDDA

Hear them call and cry, _____ wheel -
Stri - do - no las - sù, _____ *li -*

ing and glid - ing, Off on the wing _____
be - ra - men - te lan - cia - ti_a vol, _____

as swift as an ar-row in flight!_____ They
a vol co - me frec-ce, gli au - gel._____ Di -

sail up to the clouds where the sun___ is
sfi - da - no le nu - bi e'l sol___ co -

rid - ing, For - ev - er climb -
cen - te, e van - no, e van -

(with an outburst of feeling)

- ing to the heav'n - ly height._____
- no per le vie del ciel._____

there._____ How like my
dor:_____ se guo - no an -

heart they pur - sue a vis - ion of
ch'es - si un so - gno, u - na chi -

rap - - ture, For - ev - er
me - - ra, e van - no, e

climb - - ing in the gold - en
van - - no fra le nu - bi

Love Duet

E ALLOR PERCHÈ

Original key: B-flat

SILVIO

p *(with intense feeling)*

Can you de-ny me___ all I have prayed for,
E al-lor per-chè, di',___ tu m'hai stre-ga - to

Can-not your heart___ per - suade you to stay?___
se vuoi la - sciar - - mi sen - za pie - tà?___

This is the hour___ that kiss-es were made for,
Quel ba-cio tuo___ per - chè me l'hai da - - to

Would you re-gret it and turn a - way?
fra spa-smi ar-den - ti di vo - lut - tà?

(with growing warmth)

Have you for-got - ten all that we dreamed of?
Se tu scor-da - sti l'o - re fu - ga - ci,

Mine is a dream that will nev - er de-part.
io non lo pos - so, e vo - glio an-cor,

passionately

Love me for - ev - - er give me your kiss - es, your dear car
que' spa-smi ar-den - ti, que' cal - di ba - ci, che tan - ta

A little faster

NEDDA (*overwhelmed with emotion*)

side,   hap - py   in   Par - a - dise!_____   All   that   I
mor   cal - ma e   tran - quil - la!_____   A   te   mi

live   for   is   to dream a - bout   you,   Life___ has   no
do - no;   su   me so - lo im - pe - ra.   Ed___   io ti

mean - ing_____   if I must live with - out   you!
pren - do_____   e m'ab - ban - do - no in - te -   ra!

Broadly, with ecstasy
NEDDA

Here   in_____ my   heart!_____
Tut -   - to_____ scor - diam!_____

SILVIO

Here   in_____   my
Tut -   - to_____ scor -

Play a Part!

RECITAR!

Original key: A minor

Play a part! With my
Re - ci - tar! Men-tre

mind verg-ing on mad - ness,   I don't know what I'm   do - ing,   or   what I'm
pre - so dal de - li - rio,   non so più quel che   di - co   e   quel che

say - ing!   And yet Pa - gliac-cio   must   go on!   Bah!
fac - cio!   Ep-pur è d'uo-po,   sfor - za - ti!   Bah!

You must a - muse_ them with sob - bing and sigh - ing,
Tra - mu - ta in laz - zi lo spa - smo ed il pian - to;

And show them all how the art - ist plays his part. Ah!___
in u - na smor-fia il sin - ghiozzo e'l do - lor— Ah!___

Laugh then, Pa - gliac - cio, for the love that is dy - ing, Laugh through the
Ri - di, Pa - gliac - cio, sul tuo a - mo - re in - fran - to! Ri - di del

pain that is des - troy - ing your heart.___
duol che t'av - ve - le - na il cor!___

Harlequin's Serenade
O COLOMBINA

Allegretto

Original key: A minor

(As though tuning up)

HARLEQUIN

Oh _____ Co - lum - bine, your faith - ful Har - le - quin is near,
O _____ Co - lom - bi - na, il te - ne - ro fi - do Ar - lec - chin

p lightly

O - pen and hear! _____
è a te vi - cin! _____

Hear _____ how I sigh, be-cause I'm dy - ing for you to ap - pear! _____
Di _____ te chia - man - do, e so-spi - ran-do a-spet-ta il po - ve - rin! _____

Show _____ me your love-ly face and let me know my fate.
La _____ tua fac - cet - ta mo-stra-mi, ch'io vo' ba - ciar

Why hes - i - tate?_____ Oh, don't you miss me, Oh, won't you
sen - za tar - dar_____ la tua boc - cuc - cia. A - mor mi

kiss me, My love will kill me if I have to wait!
cruc - cia! A - mor mi cruc-cia e mi sta a tor-men - tar!

_Ah!_____ Why must I have to wait?_____
_Ah!_____ e mi sta a tor-men - tar!_____

mf

p
O - ____ pen your win-dow, Co-lum-bine! Oh let me in!
O_____ Co-lom-bi - na, schiu-di-mi il fi - ne-strin,

p

Your Har - le - quin___ sighs on your door - step,
che a te vi - cin___ di te chia - man - do,

Dies here on your step,___ So why not let me in?
e so - spi - ran - do___ è il po - ve - ro Ar - lec - chin!

Your poor Har-le - quin,___
A te___ vi - cin___

Let me in!
è Ar - lec - chin!

Gavotte

GUARDA, AMOR MIO

Tempo di Gavotta *(elegantly)*

Original key: E

Behold, my love, the lus-cious lunch that I have been pre-par-ing! Be-hold, my love, the wond-rous wine that we two shall be shar-ing! Ah! Af -

Guar - da, a - mor mio, che splen-di - da ce - net - ta pre-pa-rà - i! Guar - da, a - mor mio, che net - ta - re di - vi - no t'ap - por - ta - i! Ah! L'a -

p lightly

COLUMBINE

HARLEQUIN

COLUMBINE *(without slowing down)*

HARLEQUIN

(without slowing down)

A Note About the Editor

Henry W. Simon was, until recently, music critic for the newspaper *PM*, and in 1944 was elected chairman of the Music Critics Circle of New York. He studied music privately. In 1933 he earned the degree of Doctor of Philosophy at Columbia University, where he gave graduate and undergraduate courses in literature and music for twelve years.